LANGUAGE AND LANGUAGE LEARNING

Language Laboratory Facilities

LANGUAGE AND LANGUAGE LEARNING

General Editors: RONALD MACKIN *and* PETER STREVENS

The suggestions contained in this guide are presented to assist effective planning, selection, installation, and operation of language laboratory facilities. The guide, however, is not to be considered, either directly or indirectly, an endorsement of any manufacturer's product by the Office of Education.

RALPH C. M. FLYNT

ASSOCIATE COMMISSIONER

FOR EDUCATIONAL RESEARCH

AND DEVELOPMENT

Language Laboratory Facilities

Technical Guide for
their Selection, Purchase,
Use, and Maintenance

A. S. HAYES

London
OXFORD UNIVERSITY PRESS
1968

Oxford University Press, Ely House, London, W.1

GLASGOW NEW YORK TORONTO MELBOURNE WELLINGTON
CAPE TOWN SALSIBURY IBADAN NAIROBI LUSAKA ADDIS ABABA
BOMBAY CALCUTTA MADRAS KARACHI LAHORE DACCA
KUALA LUMPUR HONG KONG TOKYO

Bibliography, notes and emendations
© Oxford University Press, 1968

The original version of this volume was produced by the United States
Government Printing Office (Washington, D.C., 1963) under Super-
intendent of Documents Catalog No. FS 5.221:21024. It was prepared
pursuant to a contract between the Office of Education, U.S. Department of Health, Education and Welfare, and the Electronic Industries
Association, 1721 DeSales Street, Washington, D.C. The technical and
non-pedagogical chapters were written with the advice and assistance of
electronics industry representatives, including members of the National
Audio-Visual Association. The drawings and editorial work were done
by Howard W. Sams & Co., Inc., 4300 West 62 Street, Indianapolis,
Indiana.

PRINTED IN GREAT BRITAIN BY HEADLEY BROTHERS LTD
109 KINGSWAY LONDON WC2 AND ASHFORD KENT

Foreword

The national need for citizens with competence in modern foreign
languages has brought about widespread use of electro-mechanical
devices to provide the necessary student practice in listening and speaking. During the past fifteen years, educators and electronics specialists
have been experimenting with language facilities, usually by modifying
equipment components which were originally designed for other
purposes.

These pioneering efforts established promising new patterns of instructional procedures and facilities which are being adopted by large
numbers of schools as an integral part of a nationwide commitment to
strengthen modern foreign-language teaching. The rapid growth,
diversity, and newness of these electronic aids to language learning
created the need for a study of the most effective systems of such equipment and their related technical specifications.

To meet this need, the U.S. Office of Education initiated a study,
under Title VII of the National Defense Education Act, with the Elect-
ronic Industries Association for the preparation of this *Guide for the Selection, Purchase, Use and Maintenance of Language Laboratory Facilities.*

An Office of Education committee composed of staff members repres-
enting Titles III, VI, and VII prepared the educational and technical
criteria which served as the basis for a cooperative study of the technical
considerations by representatives of the Electronic Industries Association.

The author of the guide, Alfred S. Hayes, foreign-language consultant, was chosen because of his unique qualifications to collect and
evaluate pertinent research from the many fields related to this study.

This publication sets forth conclusions reached by the Office of
Education and the electronics industry concerning educational
and technical matters which affect the ultimate competence of users of
modern foreign languages.

Editor's Preface

Although this book was first published in 1963, it remains unique even in 1968. No other work describes in terms comprehensible to the non-specialist the basic factors which determine the design, specification and operation of language laboratories. Such developments as have occurred since the first publication of this book are in general confined to changes of detail (e.g. different approaches to the lay-out of booths, or improvements in the design of tape decks) rather than alterations in the concept of language laboratories.

The book will be of especial interest to administrators and manufacturers as well as to teachers, since it was written specifically for their guidance. The original work arose, in fact, out of collaboration between representatives of the language teaching profession and of the electronics industry, in the United States.

This edition has been to some degree Anglicized. A number of vocabulary changes have been made; some specifically American usages have been deleted; some references have been up-dated. But the book remains basically Mr Hayes' original text, and he has himself been associated in its revision.

One major change which has been made in this publication, compared with the original American edition, is the addition of a bibliography. Teachers embarking for the first time on the use of language laboratory techniques (and indeed those already so engaged) often want to read further in the subject. With the agreement of Mr Hayes we have added as an Appendix to the book the *Select Bibliography for Audio-Visual and Language Laboratory Teaching* compiled for the Audio-Visual Language Association. Grateful acknowledgement is made to AVLA for their permission to print this Bibliography.

PETER STREVENS

University of Essex
February 1968

Preface to the Bibliography

The short bibliography of books and articles on audio-visual and audio-lingual materials, methods and technology, which is Appendix B in this book, is a continuation of the work begun by Mr D. S. Kenrick, M.A., formerly on the language teaching staff of Ealing Technical College and at present a lecturer at the Thames-side Adult Education Centre, Gravesend, Kent, who compiled two mimeographed editions, the second of which appeared in July 1964, for the membership of the Audio-Visual Language Association. In the autumn of 1965, I undertook to revise his work and I should like to thank both Mr Kenrick and the Executive Committee of AVLA for their permission to publish this new edition as an appendix to the present book.

The bibliography does not claim to be in any way comprehensive but rather attempts to provide a representative sample of the very large number of books and especially articles on audio-visual and audio-lingual techniques and allied subjects that have appeared during the last five years. It was decided to include almost nothing earlier than 1962, since much of this earlier material is now out of date, and to restrict the selection largely, although not entirely, to those periodicals which are more easily obtainable in this country or are British publications. The bibliography contains 358 entries, including cross-references, of which by far the greater number refer to articles in journals and periodical publications.

J. B. KAY

University of Essex
February 1968

Contents

1 What Is a Language Laboratory?

INTRODUCTION

A language laboratory is a classroom or other area containing electronic and mechanical equipment designed and arranged to make foreign-language learning more effective than is usually possible without it.

Language laboratories may be very broadly classified into two groups according to the way they fit into the school's plan of operation. One group includes all *class* systems; according to this plan of operation, laboratory work is scheduled by classes. The second group includes all *library* systems; according to this plan of operation, laboratory work is conceived as comparable to library work, students attending at their own convenience, or scheduled at times unrelated to their language class meetings.

Functional and budgetary considerations make it necessary that many different features in many different physical arrangements be available to either type of system. So that the reader may become generally familiar with typical installations, a representative system from each group is described here, and some common terms are defined. Chapter 4: Language Laboratory Systems, will describe and classify the various possibilities in some detail.

In both class and library systems, students sit at tables, and may be partially isolated from one another by dividing partitions. The space allotted to a single student is called a *student position* or *student station*; if dividing partitions are used, the resulting semi-enclosed individual space is called a *booth*.

A TYPICAL CLASS INSTALLATION, WITH MANY FEATURES OPTIONAL

A. Equipment under the control of the teacher

(1) One or more *tape recorders* which serve as sources of recorded sound to which students listen. Disc (record) players are also used.

The tape recorders may also be used for recording students' voices for testing purposes. A single tape recorder or disc player connected for student listening is called a *programme source*.

(2) A telephone headset for listening to the programme source or to one or more students. A telephone headset may be called simply a *headset, earphones*, or *headphones*. The term *headphones* will henceforth be used in this guidebook.

(3) A *microphone* for talking to one or more members of the class (intercom facilities), or for recording lesson material.

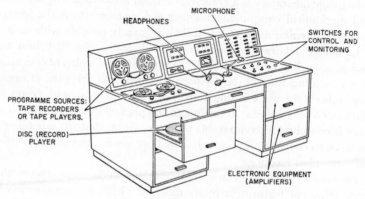

Fig. 1.1. Teacher's console.

(4) A system of switches which permits the teacher to listen to individual students. The facilities thus provided are called *monitoring facilities*.

(5) Suitable electronic equipment which amplifies the sound so that it may be distributed to the student positions. See *amplifier* in the glossary on page 5.

(6) A housing for all the above equipment, usually called the *teacher's console*. The teacher's console is normally located at the front of the room, so that the teacher faces the class in the normal manner, but its physical location is not critical. It is sometimes installed at the side or rear of the room. When programme sources and amplifying equipment are housed separately from the various controls which operate them and located at some distance from the console, the equipment is said to be *remote-controlled*. See Chapter 4, pages 36-7.

B. Equipment under the control of the student

   (1) Headphones through which the student listens.

   (2) A *volume control* by which the student adjusts the volume of the programme source for comfortable listening.

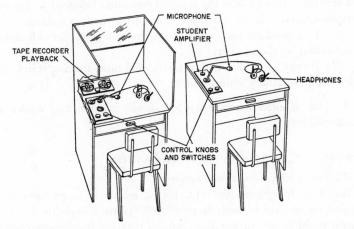

Fig. 1.2. Student equipment.

   (3) A microphone, used to fulfil one or more of three functions:

     (a) To permit the student to hear his own voice amplified in the headphones as he responds to the voice on the tape. Headphones so connected are called *activated headphones* and the entire system is called an *audio-active system*. This arrangement permits the student a greater sense of isolation than would otherwise be possible while at the same time giving his own voice the same amplified quality as that coming to him from the programme source. It usually requires a *student amplifier* at the student position.

     (b) In conjunction with a tape recorder, to permit the student to record his voice.

     (c) To permit the student to respond to the teacher through the intercom system, if provided.

   (4) A tape recorder, with its various control knobs and switches. It may be connected in various ways to perform various functions:

     (a) To record lesson material coming from the programme source. If the teaching material can be thus recorded, the student can then proceed independently of the programme at his own individual learning rate.

(b) To record his own voice while he is responding to the voice on the tape as it comes to him either directly from the programme source or from his recording of it. When he plays back appropriate sections of this tape, he will hear the original recording followed by his own responses to it. This permits him to compare the two versions.

(c) To record his own voice for testing purposes, for subsequent evaluation by the teacher.

(d) It may be loaded with pre-recorded tape, making it independent of an auxiliary sound source.

C. A system of either wired or wireless circuits interconnecting teacher and student equipment

A TYPICAL LIBRARY INSTALLATION

A. Programme sources and control equipment

In this type of system (see Fig. 1.3) a relatively large number of programme sources is used. Since recordings are seldom made at the control position, the programme sources may be simple tape players. Ideally, there would be enough tape players to permit simultaneous operation of all levels of all languages being taught. The seating capacity must be appropriately large. Amplifying equipment is required just as in the class system described above. Monitoring facilities are not usually provided.

B. Equipment under the control of the student

Student equipment possibilities are identical with those used in the class system. The number of individual tape recorders installed may be sufficient only for testing needs, and to provide for different individual learning rates in special cases. When pre-recorded lesson tapes are not provided, there may be a selector switch for choosing the proper lesson tape. An alternative arrangement simply allocates specific student positions to particular languages or courses; no student selector switch is then required, wiring is simpler, but the system is less flexible.

Library systems are found almost exclusively in large colleges and universities. Since students normally live on or near the campus, they fit in their language laboratory practice at times which best suit their individual schedules, just as they would go to the library to study for any course.

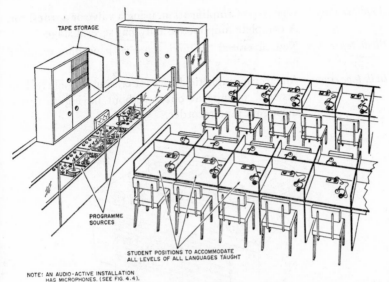

NOTE: AN AUDIO-ACTIVE INSTALLATION
HAS MICROPHONES. (SEE FIG. 4.4).

Fig. 1.3. A typical library installation.

Secondary schools, with their more rigid schedules and totally different student circumstances, find it very difficult to work with this type
of system. Yet it is only the library system, or facilities which provide an
individual portable recorder for each student, which can make full
provision for the *extra* hours of practice time which can be so important
in foreign-language learning.[1] School administrators experimenting
with the possibilities of irregular scheduling, school days of varying
lengths, and other departures from current practice, should investigate
carefully the possibilities of the library system, or a system of portable
recorders. See Chapter 3, pages 22-3.

SOME COMMON TAPE-RECORDING TERMS[2]

Amplifier: A general term referring to an arrangement of elec-
                 tronic parts, including valves or transistors, capable of
                 changing a weak signal into a stronger one.

---

[1] See also Chapter 2, pp. 14-15, Chapter 3, p. 17 for a discussion of practice time
considerations.
[2] For a more complete glossary of language laboratory terms, see Joseph C.
Hutchinson, *Modern Foreign Languages in High School: The Language Laboratory* (U.S.
Department of Health, Education and Welfare, OE-27013, Bulletin 1961, No. 23),
48-56.

Amplifier stage: One step of amplification, using a valve or a transistor. A complete amplifier usually has several stages.

Blank tape: New or erased magnetic tape with nothing recorded on it.

Bulk tape eraser: An electro-magnetic device for erasing a whole reel (or cassette) of tape at once, without having to run it through a tape recorder.

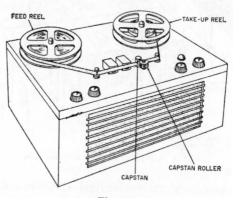

Fig. 1.4.

Capstan: The rotating shaft, connected to the motor in a tape recorder, which moves the tape forward in conjunction with the capstan roller.

Capstan roller: A rubber-like cylinder which squeezes the tape tightly against the capstan to assure forward movement.

Cartridge: Stylus mounting on a record-player pick-up.
See also *Cassette*.

Cassette: A device, similar to a reel, which holds blank or recorded tape, and is placed in operating position by a snap-in motion, avoiding tape handling and threading. (Also called a *cartridge*.)

Channel: (1) Loosely, a programme source.

(2) The electrical path from programme source to headphones. Each programme source requires a separate channel.

(3) Used in compound words to refer to the design features of a tape recorder which permit it to

record and play back either one track, or two or more independently or simultaneously. See *Single-channel recorder*, *Dual-channel recorder*.

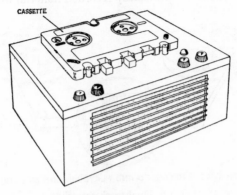

CASSETTE

Fig. 1.5.

(4) Used in compound words to refer to the design features of an amplifier which permit it to amplify either one signal, or two or more independently or simultaneously. Thus, a single-channel amplifier can carry only one signal at a time, while a dual-channel amplifier can carry two.

Counter: A device similar to the total mileage indicator in a car, which permits indexing the location of different recorded items within a single reel of tape, and thereby facilitates finding them.

Deck: See *Tape deck*.

Drive wheel: A rubber or rubber-like wheel which is part of the internal mechanism in a tape recorder.

Dual-channel amplifier: See *Channel*.

Dual-channel recorder: A tape recorder which can record or play two tracks independently or simultaneously. A modification of the dual-channel recorder provides the 'record-compare' facilities included in many language laboratories.

Dual-track recording: A recording made by a dual-channel recorder, using both channels.

Dub: To make tape duplicates; to copy tape; to insert a por-
                tion in an already prepared tape; a copy of a tape.

Erase head: The electro-magnetic device on a tape recorder which
                removes previously recorded material from the tape.

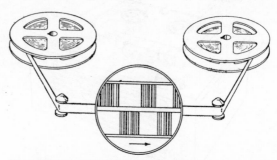

BOTH TRACKS RECORDED AND PLAYED IN ONE DIRECTION

Fig. 1.6. Dual-track recording.

Fast forward: Rapid movement of tape in the forward direction,
                  from feed reel to take-up reel.

Feed reel: The full reel of tape, which empties onto the take-up
                  reel when a tape is recorded or played.

Four-track   See *Quarter-track recording.*
recording:

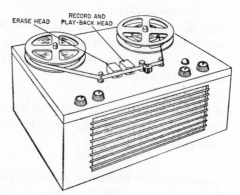

Fig. 1.7.

Full-track   A tape recorder with a record head capable of making
recorder: and playing a full-track recording. It can play a half-
                  track recording only if one track is blank.

Full-track recording: A recording occupying the full width of a quarter-inch tape. Sometimes called *single-track recording*, but this term is not recommended.

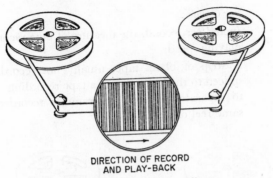

DIRECTION OF RECORD
AND PLAY-BACK

Fig. 1.8. Full-track recording.

Gain control: The terms *gain control*, *level control*, and *volume control* are often used interchangeably to refer to a control which adjusts the loudness of what is heard. In the latter sense, *volume control* is ordinarily used by non-technical people, *gain control* or *level control* by technicians and engineers. Strictly speaking, *gain control* is the proper term for any control which adjusts the amplification (gain) of an amplifier, regardless of the effect on the ear. *Level control* is the proper term for any control used to set some operating point (level) in any electronic circuit, often by observing a meter or other electronic measuring device.

Half-track recorder: A tape recorder with a record head capable of making a half-track recording, and playing both half-track and full-track recordings.

Half-track recording: A recording occupying half the width of a quarter-inch tape. Two different half-track recordings may be made on a single quarter-inch tape, each recording beginning at opposite ends of the tape. Sometimes called a *dual-track* recording, but this term is best reserved for a different application. See *Dual-track recording*.

Head: See *Erase head, Playback head, Record head.*

Head   A service instrument which removes the residual
demagnetizer: magnetism which accumulates in tape-recorder heads
                       as a result of use.

Idler wheel: See *Drive wheel.*

Indexer: See *Counter.*

Ips.; i/s: Inches *per second*, the measure of tape recording and
                       playing speed.

Leader tape: A strip of blank tape, usually not recording tape,
                       spliced to the beginning of a tape recording. Also used
                       to separate different programmes recorded on the
                       same reel of tape.

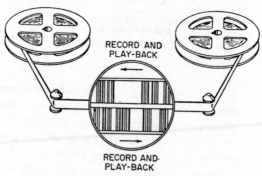

Fig. 1.9. Half-track recording.

Level control: See *Gain control.*

Magnetic tape: A ribbon of magnetically sensitive material on which
                       sound is recorded by a tape recorder. Except in certain
                       elaborate experimental situations, quarter-inch tape is
                       universally used in language-laboratory applications.

Monaural: See *Channel, Single-channel recorder.*

Pause control: A special control feature which stops the tape move-
                       ment without disturbing any other functions or opera-
                       tions of the recorder. Tape movement resumes
                       instantaneously when this spring-operated lever is
                       released.

Playback head: The magnetic device on a tape recorder which con-
                       verts patterns of magnetization on a recorded tape into

electrical impulses which are then amplified and converted into sound.

Player:	See *Tape player.*
Power amplifier:	An amplifier furnishing sufficient signal power to operate a loudspeaker.
Preamp:	See *Preamplifier.*
Preamplifier:	An amplifier stage or stages designed to raise the very weak signal from a microphone, a tape head, or certain record-player pick-up cartridges, to some predetermined level. A preamplifier will not operate a loudspeaker directly.
Prerecorded tape:	Tape which contains lesson or other materials, recorded prior to use in instruction, either commercially or by the instructional staff.
Quarter-track recording:	A recording consisting of two separate dual-track recordings; four separate recorded tracks on the tape.
Recorded tape:	Magnetic tape with a recording on it.
Recorder:	See *Tape recorder.*
Record head:	The magnetic device on a tape recorder which converts amplified electrical impulses from a microphone into a correspondingly varying magnetic field, which puts 'sound' on the tape in the form of invisible patterns of magnetization. With appropriate switching, it may also serve as a playback head.
Recording speed:	See *Tape speed.*
Recording tape:	See *Magnetic tape.*
Reel:	The spool, usually of plastic, which holds blank or recorded tape.
Rewind:	Rapid movement of the tape in the reverse direction, from take-up reel to feed reel.
Signal:	Designates whatever is supposed to be heard over a reproducing system, as distinguished from unwanted noise.
Single-channel amplifier:	See *Channel.*

Single-channel recorder:	A full-track or half-track tape recorder which can record or play only one track at a time.
Solenoid:	An electromagnet, often used to provide instantaneous control of a mechanical switch.
Speed:	See *Tape speed.*
Splice:	To attach two pieces of tape; also, a patch connecting two pieces of tape.
Splicing tape:	A special adhesive material for splicing recording tape.
Stage:	See *Amplifier stage.*
Take-up reel:	The empty reel which fills with tape from the feed reel as a tape is recorded or played.
Tape:	See *Magnetic tape.*
Tape cartridge:	See *Cassette.*
Tape cassette:	See *Cassette.*
Tape deck:	Strictly, a tape recorder, minus the power amplifier required to operate a loudspeaker, but usually including a preamplifier. If no reference to amplifiers is intended, *tape deck* means the same thing as *tape transport.*
Tape player:	A tape programme source having only a play-back head. It can thus play tapes, but cannot record or erase them.
Tape recorder:	A single machine capable of recording sound on magnetic tape and reproducing it or erasing it at will.
Tape speed:	The speed with which the tape moves past the heads when recording or playing. The two common speeds are $7\frac{1}{2}$ and $3\frac{3}{4}$ inches per second (ips).
Tape transport:	Strictly, that part of the tape recorder which transfers the tape from reel to reel, or which operates a tape cassette. It also supports the heads under a common cover. Although properly used without reference to any amplifying equipment, the term is also used loosely to mean *tape deck.*
Thread:	To run the loose end of tape from the feed reel to the take-up reel in such a way that the machine is ready to play or record.

Track: The magnetized path made on a tape when a recording is made. Different physical head designs produce tracks of different widths.

Transistor: A miniature electronic device which performs the functions of a valve.

Transport: See *Tape transport*.

Virgin tape: Blank magnetic tape which has never been used.

Volume control: See *Gain control*.

VU meter: A meter which indicates the signal level of either the recording signal or the playback signal. It is used to establish the VU (volume units) or the eventual 'loudness' of the recording.

2 Why a Language Laboratory?

Traditional foreign-language instruction was dedicated largely to the teaching of reading, approached through the study of the rules of grammar. The basic approach, with only minor variations, was extensive translation. But recent years have witnessed a shift of emphasis in language teaching and learning. It has become a matter of national self-interest to increase the number of citizens who can understand and speak a foreign language. This shift of emphasis is paralleled by recent advances in linguistic science and allied fields, which have contributed to a new view of language and language learning. In this view, understanding and speaking a foreign language are regarded first as essential primary objectives in themselves, then as a sound basis for systematically acquiring the important reading and writing skills on which the affairs of a literate society so heavily depend. Central to this view is the observation that understanding and speaking are to a large extent matters of habit, rather than matters of knowledge.

The only known way to form habits is through practice. Learning a foreign language is in this respect much like learning to play a musical instrument. No one questions that the music student must practise, if he wants to learn to play, say, the piano, since it is obvious that no amount of study of musical notation alone will teach anyone to play. Yet failure to make satisfactory progress in a foreign language has been traditionally attributed to insufficient *study* rather than to the real cause, insufficient practice. Even grammar, which in this view of language learning is not discarded, as is sometimes supposed, is internalized more by extensive practice in using the most frequent grammatical constructions of the language than by studying statements about them, although such statements have their place.

The musical analogy may be pursued even further, although the parallel is not exact. The mechanics of piano-playing must be automatic, or the student will never be able to concentrate on reproducing the 'meaning' the composer intended, much less go on to successful improvisation or composition. Successful control of a foreign language is even more exacting, for the speaker constantly improvises, often producing genuine, natural utterances which neither he nor anyone else has said before in exactly that way. Both musical and language improvisation are, however, tightly bound to sounds and constructions to which members of the same cultural community can successfully react, and without firm control of these sounds and these constructions, the improvisation will be chaotic, and the 'message' will not be understood. The composer, and the poet, exploit this firm control to experiment with new arrangements to convey both familiar and unfamiliar meanings.

Practice is, then, essential to understanding and speaking a foreign language. A competent teacher, who makes the best possible use of classroom time, and has access to good materials, can, indeed, successfully provide the kind of practice required. But it is difficult, often exhausting, for a live teacher to provide, throughout countless repetitions, the consistently authentic model and the carefully sequenced progression of drills which efficient practice requires. *To provide this practice is the fundamental role of the language laboratory.*

SPECIFIC ADVANTAGES PROVIDED BY THE LANGUAGE LABORATORY

(1) In a language laboratory all students present can practise aloud simultaneously, yet individually. In a class of 30 students, 29 are not idle while one is busy.

(2) The teacher is free to focus his attention on the individual student's performance without interrupting the work of the group.

(3) Certain language laboratory facilities can provide for differences in learning rates.

(4) The language laboratory can provide authentic, consistent, untiring models of speech for imitation and drill.

(5) The use of headphones gives a sense of isolation, intimate contact with the language, equal clarity of sound to all students, and facilitates complete concentration.

(6) Recordings can provide many native voices. Without such variety it is common for students to be able to understand only the teacher.

(7) The language laboratory facilitates testing of each student for listening comprehension. It has generally been impracticable for the unaided teacher to test this skill.

(8) The language laboratory facilitates testing of the speaking ability of each student in a class. It has generally been impracticable for the unaided teacher to test this skill.

(9) Some teachers, for reasons beyond their control, do not themselves have sufficient preparation in understanding and speaking the foreign language. The language laboratory provides these teachers with an opportunity to improve their own proficiency.

(10) The language laboratory makes it possible to divide a class into teacher-directed and machine-directed groups.

(11) Certain language laboratory facilities can enhance the student's potential for evaluating his own performance.

(12) Given specially-designed instructional materials, the language laboratory can provide technical facilities for efficient self-instruction.[1]

---

[1] See the section on programmed instruction in Chapter 3.

3 Planning for a Language Laboratory

CRITERIA FOR EQUIPMENT SELECTION

There follow a number of criteria for the selection of language laboratory equipment.

(1) *The criterion of adequate practice time*

In view of the indispensable requirement of frequent, regular practice, equipment should be provided to allow at least twenty minutes use per class day per student. This means that, considering the number of students involved and the funds and space available, it may be advisable to install equipment that is far simpler than that described in Chapter 1. Effective use of good materials can begin with a single tape recorder or record-player in each classroom at any level.

(2) *The criterion of evaluation of progress*

In view of the nature and importance of regular testing, provision should be made for tests of speaking ability. Students cannot be expected to learn to speak the foreign language if that skill is not to be evaluated regularly by tests. This means that there must be access to a number of tape recorders, sufficient to permit testing without serious disturbance of class schedules.

The examination function is particularly important, because much of the revolution now under way in foreign language teaching and examining focuses upon the need to teach students to speak, as well as to understand, read, and write.

(3) *The criterion of extended practice*

In view of the requirement of frequent, regular practice, provision should be made for more work with recorded native models than can be supplied in the presence of the teacher. This criterion of outside-of-class or homework stems from the close analogy between learning a foreign language and learning to play a musical instrument. In neither case are we doing complete justice to the student's need for practice if we confine his efforts to the time we can afford in the presence of his teacher. This criterion may be met either by extra practice in the language laboratory using only supervisory personnel, or by the use of homework discs or tape recordings supplied as part of the course materials.

(4) *The criterion of teacher readiness*

As a general rule, language laboratory equipment should not be installed until the teachers have developed a readiness to use it. 'Readiness', in the sense intended here, should never be expected to include the technical skill necessary to maintain the equipment, but only the pedagogical and mechanical skills necessary to teach with the machines, and familiarity with the proper instructional materials which the use of machines presupposes. This means that a programme of in-service training for teachers should be planned well in advance of the purchase of equipment. Lacking such a programme, it may be wise to begin with an installation as simple as a single tape recorder in each room, perhaps including multiple headphones, and adding other equipment in stages. With proper planning, this can be done without significant loss or increase in cost.

If the plan can envisage all that might be desired in the final stage, including electronic compatibility of the components to be installed at later stages, certain elements, such as wiring, can be provided at only nominal extra cost along with the initial simple installation. Thus, successive phases in the development of the system would involve only the addition of new components, with no expense for replacements or rewiring.

It is inevitable that with the rapid development of new kinds of teaching materials and the extraordinary advances in the field of electronics, some items of equipment will become obsolete. However, our inability to describe accurately the language laboratory fifteen years hence should not deter any school from making the best use of the equipment that is now available.

LANGUAGE LABORATORIES AND THE PRIMARY SCHOOL

The special pupil-teacher rapport necessary in the primary school, the shorter attention span of younger children, and the special administrative problems tend to militate against the use of full-scale language laboratories at this level. The use of tape recorders and simple multiple-headphone arrangements does seem justified, especially in view of the acute shortage of adequately trained primary school teachers to serve as native or near-native models. Continued research and experimentation on the use of such equipment in the primary school should be encouraged, however, since concrete evidence of the way in which its effectiveness differs for different age groups is almost wholly lacking.

STEP-BY-STEP PLANNING: THE USE OF CONSULTANTS

In planning for a language laboratory, it is often difficult to determine just what steps should be taken, and in what order. A review of the practical and theoretical problems involved, and suggestions for their solution, is given in Edward M. Stack, *The Language Laboratory and Modern Language Teaching*, Second Edition (New York, Oxford University Press, 1966), 24-37. The reader is also referred to an article by the present writer, entitled 'Procedures for language laboratory planning'.[1]

In the above article, and elsewhere in the now extensive literature on language laboratories, the consumer is advised to obtain the services of a professional consultant. Since the use of such consultants is relatively new in the language field, some suggestions are given here for identifying and qualifying specialists in this field, and for making the most effective use of their services.

Before a consultant is actually chosen, it is most important to try to identify as specifically as possible the problem or problems you wish him to help solve. Following a period of preparatory study, administrators, purchasing personnel, and the language teaching staff should try to frame specific questions. Time thus spent in assembling a careful statement of problems can both increase the ultimate value of the consultant's contribution and reduce the cost to the institution by making efficient use of his time.

It is convenient to consider three possible statements of the consultant's role:

(1) If the requirements are highly specialized, as is sometimes the case in large university installations requiring custom design, the institution may need engineering services beyond those usually supplied

---

[1] *The Bulletin* of the National Association of Secondary School Principals, 46/272, 123-35.

by language laboratory companies. In such cases the consultant must be a qualified electronics engineer, with experience in the design of complex audio distribution systems. In addition, he should be or become familiar with the special requirements of recording and reproducing systems to be used for foreign-language instruction, as set forth in Chapter 5 of this guidebook. Similar qualifications are required for making evaluations or tests of the comparative performance characteristics of samples of equipment, e.g. various makes and models of headphones and microphones which have been submitted for approval.

Such personnel can be located through electronics consulting firms, electrical engineering departments of colleges and universities, and radio and television broadcasting stations.

(2) The consultant is to take over the entire job of advising and assisting the institution in all aspects of the development of its new foreign-language programme. He will assist the staff with its preparatory study, discussing with them questions of theory and methodology in the light of available materials and institutional materials-adoption policies. Within stated budgetary limits, he will develop a practical language laboratory programme, which will include a statement of needed equipment functions, specific recommendations for implementing them, adequate provision for expansion, and a set of specifications tailored to the precise needs of the institution. In making his recommendations, he will reduce the large field of potential suppliers to perhaps three or four whose products seem best suited to the requirements, taking into consideration the preferences, if any, of the staff, arrived at through preparatory study and observation of actual language laboratory installations in operation at other institutions. He will thus relieve the institutional staff of the wearisome task of listening to the presentations of dozens of competing firms. He may be called upon to help evaluate specific items of equipment as suggested in the proposals of the companies of choice, and to make actual engineering suggestions requiring a high degree of technical competence. Upon completion of the laboratory installation, he may be called upon to conduct such practical performance tests as are feasible, to assume the responsibility for final approval, and to assist the institution in setting up a suitable preventive-maintenance programme.

At the present writing, there are very few consultants both available and competent to assume this kind of extensive and time-consuming responsibility. The kinds of competence required are extremely diverse, and will ultimately be supplied by responsible consulting firms who will employ different specialists as needed, and consolidate their efforts.

(3) Practical use of a consultant at present will, therefore, usually be based on a more restricted view of his contribution. The institution may have some specific questions on methodology or materials, but has reasonably firm convictions concerning its requirements, and wishes them translated into a practical set of equipment specifications. Or, the institution may have already prepared tentative specifications and merely wish them to be examined for technical accuracy. The consultant may or may not be employed to approve the final installation.

Such a consultant should have the following qualifications: (a) he should have a broad background of experience in language teaching, and be thoroughly familiar with audio-lingual theory and methodology; (b) he should have had several years of experience as supervisor or director of a language laboratory; (c) in view of these requirements, he is unlikely to be an electronics engineer, but his background should include electronics experience at the technician level, and his language laboratory experience should have included actual contact with the technical details of the equipment; (d) he should not be affiliated with a company which manufactures language laboratory equipment.

The most likely source for this type of consultant will be the language laboratories of large colleges and universities. A good plan is to write to the director of such a laboratory for suggestions.

THE LANGUAGE LABORATORY AND PROGRAMMED INSTRUCTION[1]

There has been considerable recent interest in the use of the techniques of programmed instruction in many subject matter fields, including foreign languages. Briefly, programmed instruction is intended to increase efficiency, and, in some cases, to make possible efficient self-instruction. It requires exact specification of what is to be learned (terminal behaviour) and breaks up this material into optimally small units, called *frames*. The amount of new material added by successive frames is adjusted so that the possibility of error is drastically reduced.

---

[1] A detailed discussion of the principles and problems of programmed instruction, as applied to foreign language, will be found in: John B. Carroll, 'A primer of programmed instruction in foreign language teaching', *I.R.A.L.*, 1/2 (1963) 115-41.

2

It utilizes the principle of immediate reinforcement of correct responses, considered as indispensable to effective teaching and learning. It can account completely for differences in individual learning rates, since students proceed at their own pace. It is natural to inquire in what way this promising new look at learning should influence language laboratory planning, if at all.

Considerable attention has been given to the design of recorded materials for language laboratory use. The essential difference between programmed instruction and traditional language laboratory techniques lies in the tested design of the taped materials in accordance with the principles just described. But many of the efforts which have been expended on the development of techniques to increase the efficiency of language laboratory practice are not inconsistent with the basic idea of programmed instruction and, indeed, have been intuitively influenced by it.

A number of foreign-language projects experimenting with programmed instruction use only a conventional tape recorder and a workbook. Thus the language laboratory student position which is equipped with its own tape recorder meets the technical requirements of these particular teaching-machine programmes. Since, for many reasons, a number of student positions, in many cases all, will be equipped with individual tape recorders, it can be seen that adequate planning for the ultimate use of this kind of programmed instruction in the language laboratory requires only that proper wiring provisions be made for the eventual installation of complete tape recorders at each student position.

On the other hand, some of the techniques now undergoing experimental development will require presentation devices with features quite different from those usually found on the conventional tape recorder. These features raise new design problems and introduce the serious question of standardization of taped and/or visual materials and their modes of presentation. In school situations it would be unwise to consider the use of such devices at a stage of development when such use might involve permanent commitment to the programmed materials of one particular source.

Stimulated by developments in programmed instruction, small, light, portable units similar to the tape recorder, and intended for both home and school use, will soon be available. Certainly, any device or any programme designed to increase the now dubious efficiency of home practice will be welcome. It is, of course, imperative that audio quality be sufficiently high for foreign-language instruction (see Chapter 5), and that cost be low enough so that each student could be assigned his own portable unit.

The implications of programmed instruction for language laboratory planning may be summarized thus: suitable wiring to accommodate individual tape recorders at each student position in the language laboratory will provide adequately for the currently most promising of those advances in programmed instruction which include the audio-lingual aspects of foreign-language learning. Techniques involving more complex presentational devices can eventually be accommodated in the language laboratory in the same way, but lacking standardization, may invite commitment to the programmes of one particular source. Language teachers and administrators should keep abreast of developments in portable units for home and school use.

4 Language Laboratory Systems[1]

In Chapter 1 two typical language laboratory systems were briefly described and some common terms defined. This chapter will describe some of the many possible variations in such systems, and discuss the relative advantages and limitations of each. In view of the administrative complications inherent in the use of library systems in secondary schools, all of the systems discussed in this section are to be considered class systems, although both class and library systems obviously have many features in common.

The systems are described in order of complexity. The numbered advantages listed with each system refer to specific advantages provided by the language laboratory listed in Chapter 2, and are here repeated for convenient reference:

(1) In a language laboratory all students present can practise aloud simultaneously, yet individually. In a class of 30 students, 29 are not idle while one is busy.

(2) The teacher is free to focus his attention on the individual student's performance without interrupting the work of the group.

(3) Certain language laboratory facilities can provide for differences in learning rates.

(4) The language laboratory provides authentic, consistent, untiring models of speech for imitation and drill.

(5) The use of headphones gives a sense of isolation, intimate contact with the language, equal clarity of sound to all students, and facilitates complete concentration.

(6) Recordings provide many native voices. Without such variety it is common for students to be able to understand only the teacher.

---

[1] For a differently arranged, but excellently detailed discussion of language laboratory systems and the relation of their various functions to student learning activities, see Joseph C. Hutchinson, *op. cit.*, 23-35.

(7) The language laboratory facilitates testing of each student for listening comprehension. It has generally been impracticable for the unaided teacher to test this skill.

(8) The language laboratory facilitates testing of the speaking ability of each student in a class. It has generally been impracticable for the unaided teacher to test this skill.

(9) Some teachers, for reasons beyond their control, do not themselves have sufficient preparation in understanding and speaking the foreign language. The language laboratory provides these teachers with an opportunity to improve their own proficiency.

(10) The language laboratory makes it possible to divide a class into teacher-directed and machine-directed groups.

(11) Certain language laboratory facilities can enhance the student's potential for evaluating his own performance.

(12) Given specially-designed instructional materials, the language laboratory can provide technical facilities for efficient self-instruction.

SYSTEM I A: LISTEN-RESPOND

Equipment:

Tape recorder or record-player with built-in loudspeaker.[1]

Principal Functions:

Listening practice and choral drill.

Advantages:

2, 4, 6, 7, 9. This system is inexpensive and very simple to operate and manage.

Limitations:

(1) The amplifiers and loudspeakers built into equipment of this kind are frequently not of sufficient quality to provide good sound at sufficient volume. If the volume is adequate, other classes may be disturbed, depending, of course, on the acoustical properties of the room.

(2) The resulting sound, even if of adequate volume and quality, is not equal for all students in the room.

---

[1] It can be argued that this and the following simple system are not what is usually meant by a language laboratory, but they do fit the broad definition given at the beginning of Chapter 1. The listed advantages certainly cannot always be supplied by the teacher alone.

(3) The single programme source permits no provision for individual differences in rate of learning.

(4) The teacher's evaluation and correction of individual students is quite difficult.

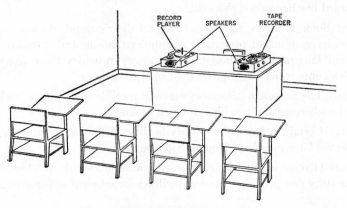

Fig. 4.1. Listen-respond, System I A.

Notes and Discussion:

This single piece of equipment, and all of the more elaborate systems discussed hereafter, requires preventive maintenance for maximum efficiency and durability. This point cannot be over-emphasized. See Chapter 7.

SYSTEM I B: LISTEN-RESPOND

Equipment:

Tape recorder or record-player with external amplifier and higher-quality speaker, or speakers, installed in or on the walls or ceiling of the room.

Principal Functions:

Same as in System I A.

Advantages:

Same as in System I A.

Limitations:

Same as in System I A, except that much better sound quality can be achieved at adequate volume, with good distribution throughout the room.

Notes and Discussion:

While excellent quality and sound distribution can be achieved by the use of several speakers, installed, for example, at intervals in the ceiling of the room, or high in two or more corners, the cost of such a

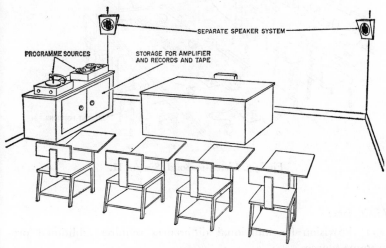

Fig. 4.2. Listen-respond, System I B.

system would be out of proportion to the gain, and, if such funds are available, serious consideration should be given to System II.

SYSTEM II: LISTEN-RESPOND

Equipment:

Tape recorder(s) or tape player(s), or record-player, with individual headphones.

Principal Functions:

Listening practice and oral drill, including small group or individualized practice to accommodate different rates of learning.

Advantages:

1, 2, 3 (but note limitations 1, 2 and 5), 4, 5, 6, 7, 9, 10.

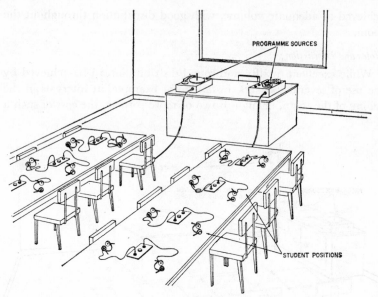

Fig. 4.3. Listen-respond, System II.

Limitations:

(1) Provision for individual differences requires additional programme sources.

(2) Individual students cannot control the machines to provide the needed number of repetitions or pauses.

(3) Without the audio-active feature of System III, the student cannot hear himself clearly as he responds, because the headphones tend to 'stop up his ears'.

(4) The teacher's evaluation and correction of individual students is easier, but still somewhat awkward.

(5) Unless the machine-drill group is isolated (e.g. by a glass partition), it cannot work aloud without disturbing the teacher-directed group.

Notes and Discussion:

(1) Unless the equipment and wiring are fixed or built-in, the task of setting up lines, headphones, etc., each time is awkward and time-consuming.

(2) Individual differences in hearing are not accommodated without a volume control for each student.

(3) Control of the programme and evaluation of students assumes that the teacher also can listen to the recorded material.

(4) Selection among multiple programme sources can be provided for by a selector switch at the student's position or at the teacher's position.

SYSTEM III: LISTEN-RESPOND (AUDIO-ACTIVE)

Equipment:

Programme sources and headphones for group practice, as in System II, plus microphones and amplification to make an audio-active system. (See Chapter 1, page 3.)

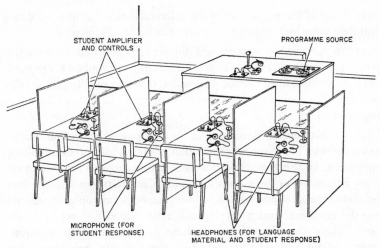

Fig. 4.4. Listen-respond (audio-active), System III.

Principal Functions:

Same as System II.

Advantages:

1, 2, 3, 4, 5, 6, 7, 9, 10, 11. This system enhances advantage 5. A properly adjusted audio-active system permits the student a greater sense of isolation than is otherwise possible, since it gives his own voice the same amplified quality as that coming to him from the programme source. Since the general level of sound heard in the headphones is constant, he is less distracted by room noise. Actual room noise is reduced because the student can now speak in a lower tone, yet without the muffled effect which is apparent in systems without the audio-active feature.

Limitations:

(1) Same as in System II.

(2) Same as in System II.

(3) The teacher's evaluation and correction of individual students is still rather awkward.

Notes and Discussion:

(1) Some of the advantage of the microphones is lost unless volume of student voice and programme source can be co-ordinated.

(2) An improperly chosen and improperly adjusted audio-active system can be troublesome. Unless the proper microphones are used, and their volume level carefully adjusted, they can readily pick up disturbing noises, including the responses of other students. See Chapter 5, pages 90 and 92.

(3) An interesting development in equipment providing audio-active facilities is the recent production of high-quality induction-loop equipment. In this type of installation, a wire loop is run around the room, connected to the output terminals of an amplifier. Signals from the chosen programme source, or the teacher's microphone, are fed into the amplifier, and a varying magnetic field is thus set up in the room. These variations are picked up and amplified in miniature battery-driven amplifiers mounted on the students' headphone sets. The headsets are also fitted with microphones, giving the student the audio-active feature. This type of equipment has all the advantages and limitations of System III, except that only one programme source, or the teacher's microphone, can be used at one time in the same room. In addition, the student is freed from wires attaching his headset to desk-mounted equipment, and the whole system is more easily portable, since a wire loop to be plugged into a suitable amplifier is the only permanent installation that is necessary.

SYSTEM IV: LISTEN-RESPOND-COMPARE (INDIVIDUAL CONTROL)

Equipment:

Same as in System III, plus separate recording facilities for individual students.

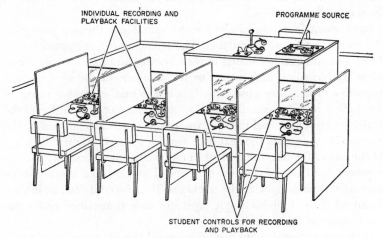

Fig. 4.5. Listen-respond-compare, System IV.

Principal Functions:

(1) Individual listening and speaking practice.

(2) Small group or individualized practice to accommodate different rates of learning.

(3) Group speaking tests.

(4) Individual control of student recorder, permitting complete adjustment to individual learning rates. The student can adjust the number of repetitions and the length of pauses as needed.

(5) The student can record his responses and compare them directly with the model in the lesson material.

(6) Master recordings for use with individual student machines can be duplicated as needed from the playback programme source or supplied on pre-recorded tapes.

Advantages:

1, 2, 3, 4, 5, 6, 7, 8, 9, 10, 11, 12.

Notes and Discussion:

To facilitate the duplicating of master tapes from the console to the student recorders, it is highly desirable that all the functions necessary for this operation can be carried out by remote control from the console. These include the simultaneous starting of all student recorders in the record mode, and preferably also the rewinding of student tapes to the start of the recording.

Such remote control facilities are also valuable in the administration of group tests of oral production. The following is a suggested procedure: The students are seated in their booths, and first identify themselves by recording their names or test numbers at the start of their respective tapes. After giving the first test item, the teacher starts all the student recorders simultaneously. Sufficient time is given for all the students to respond, and then the student recorders are stopped by the teacher. He then gives the next test item and proceeds in the same way. At the end of the test, the students' tapes contain a record only of their responses, and not of the test material. This can save a remarkable amount of time in marking the test tapes. The procedure can be further improved if the individual test tapes are then transcribed on to one continuous reel for marking.

It should be noted that solenoid-operated machines can provide instantaneous remote control stop-start action, whereas other means of control do not usually react instantaneously, and are generally unsatisfactory in the application described above. An ideal arrangement

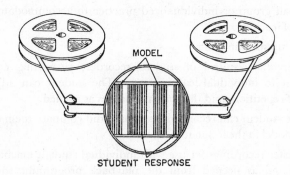

NOTE: RECORDED MATERIAL CAN BE
INADVERTENTLY ERASED.

Fig. 4.6. Single-channel recording.

would be a solenoid-operated pause control, operated by a master-switch at the console.

SINGLE-CHANNEL VERSUS DUAL-CHANNEL STUDENT RECORDERS

A single-channel recorder can, indeed, provide all of the functions of this system, but it has the disadvantage that lesson material can readily be erased by the student (see Fig. 4.6). Dual-channel recorders, on the other hand are regularly provided with a feature which places lesson

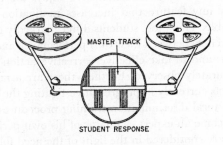

NOTE: LESSON MATERIAL (SHOWN ON THE MASTER TRACK)
CANNOT BE ERASED BY THE STUDENT

Fig. 4.7. Dual-channel recording.

material and student responses on different tracks so that they are quite independent of each other (see Fig. 4.7). The student track can thus be erased readily without affecting the lesson material recorded on the master track. If the same tapes are to be used for other lessons, a bulk eraser may be used to erase both tracks simultaneously without running the tape through a machine. Both tracks can be erased at the student position by providing erase facilities on the master channel of each student machine which can be activated only by the teacher.

THE 'COMPARE' FEATURE

There has been considerable controversy in the teaching profession concerning the merits of this facility.[1] It can be argued, for example,

---

[1] For a report on an experiment comparing the effectiveness of different kinds of language laboratory facilities, see: Sarah W. Lorge, 'Foreign language laboratories in secondary schools. A special report summarizing four years of research by the Bureau of Audio-Visual Instruction, Board of Education of the City of New York, 1959-63', *Audio-Visual Learning* 7/1.

that a beginning student is hardly a very good judge of his own pronunciation. Even if he does notice differences between his response and the model, any appreciable time-lag between originally responding and subsequently comparing weakens his impression of just what he did to cause those differences, and he may have no idea of what to do to improve his response. As a result, all he can do is try again, which he can do just as well without any recording facilities at all. Several factors must be borne in mind, however, in this connexion. Facilities permitting the student to record his own voice and compare it with a model seem to increase student motivation. He enjoys the whole procedure, and certainly any feature that increases motivation should be considered valuable. Then, too, students differ markedly in their ability to observe differences between their own performance and that illustrated by the models and to take effective corrective action if the difference has been accurately observed. Further, there are a number of experimental projects currently in progress investigating the efficiency of certain kinds of aural discrimination-training procedures in teaching the student to become an expert evaluator of his own performance. When these factors are considered in the light of the need for at least a minimum number of complete student tape recorders for the administration of group speaking tests, the installation of student recording facilities seems justified.

SYSTEM V: LISTEN-RESPOND-(COMPARE), PLUS INTERCOMMUNICATION AND MONITORING

Equipment:

The equipment of Systems III or IV, plus facilities for intercommunication and monitoring.

Principal Additional Functions:

(1) Maximum implementation of advantage 2, freedom of the teacher to focus his attention on the individual student's performance for evaluation and coaching, without interrupting the work of the group. Students tend to practise more efficiently if they realize that they are subject to evaluation at any time with or without their knowledge.

(2) Without requiring the individual student recorders of System IV, the teacher can record student speaking performance, either for examination purposes, or for subsequent analysis of both efficiency of the lesson material and the students' problems while practising. Recordings so made can serve as the basis for teacher-student critiques.

Advantages:

1, 2, 3, 4, 5, 6, 7, 8, 9, 10, 11, 12.

Limitations:

(1) It is fairly common practice for the teacher to play a single continuous lesson tape. Depending on both laboratory procedures and facilities, this material may or may not be simultaneously recorded on to the student machines for subsequent independent practice during

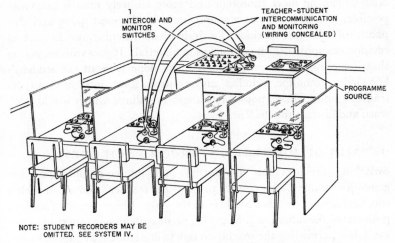

NOTE: STUDENT RECORDERS MAY BE
OMITTED. SEE SYSTEM IV.

Fig. 4.8. Intercommunication and monitoring, System V.

the same period. In either case, intercommunication with the student for coaching purposes, while it can be extremely valuable, can cause him to miss appreciable portions of the recorded lesson. This limitation can be avoided only if pre-recorded lesson tapes are available at each student position. In this case, after coaching, the student simply continues where he left off.

(2) In making student recordings via the monitoring facilities for whatever purpose, only one student can be recorded at a time unless special wiring and switching arrangements are provided. In no case is the number of students who can be so recorded simultaneously greater than the number of recorders available at the console. If this feature is to be used at all, programme sources must, of course, be complete recorders, rather than simple tape players.

(3) It should be noted that monitoring by intercom can provide only a spot-check of student errors.

Notes and Discussion:

Since ordinarily only one student can be recorded at a time, via the monitoring facilities, this technique does not provide for efficient group testing. But making occasional recordings of portions of a practice session, without the student's knowledge, is an excellent way of gathering samples of student practice for subsequent analysis. Such analysis can be more thorough and more leisurely than is otherwise possible, and can serve as a sound basis for the sequencing and emphasis of following periods, for individual coaching, or for actual revision or supplementing of the lesson materials. It goes without saying that if monitoring or recording is to be done without the student's knowledge, monitor switches and controls must introduce no extraneous noise, clicks, pops, or changes in volume which would both warn and distract the student.

DETAILS OF MONITOR-INTERCOM FACILITIES

Switching facilities for monitoring and intercommunication are generally arranged on a control panel at the teacher's console in such a way that rows of switches conform to the geographical layout of student positions in the laboratory. Many different switching arrangements are available, permitting the teacher to talk to one student at a time, to any combination of individual students and rows of students, or to the entire class (all-call feature). The all-call feature can be extremely useful, since the students are isolated from live communication by their headphones. It also provides instant alert in the case of building emergencies.

REMOTE-CONTROLLED SYSTEMS

As defined in Chapter 1, equipment is said to be remote-controlled when it is physically separated from the various controls which operate it. Programme sources, amplifying equipment, and student recorders take up classroom space which is often at a premium. If remote-controlled, they can be housed in any available area which would not normally be used as a classroom, in a different room, or even in a different building. Any of the functions of Systems III, IV or V can be implemented by remote-controlled equipment. For mass duplication of tapes it is advantageous to have all student recorders (wherever located) controlled from a single point, normally at the teacher's console.

The principal advantages of remote control of equipment which would otherwise be at the teacher's console are: (1) better utilization of space in particular school situations, as indicated above; (2) avoidance of tape handling and rewinding by the teacher. The principal advantages of remote control of equipment which would otherwise be at the student position are: (1) the possibility of malfunction due to inexpert student handling of both equipment and tape is reduced; (2) the student's concentration on the learning task at hand will be improved, because he has fewer distracting mechanical operations to perform.

If neither teacher nor student is to handle tape directly, of itself a most desirable feature, and if rewinding time is to be saved, a cassette system must be used. But see Chapter 5, pages 79-80.

In currently available remote-controlled systems tape motion is controlled and programmes are selected in either of two basically different ways: (1) by switches usually placed at the console, and (2) by means of a telephone dial system, operated by the student. The merits of either method of control must be evaluated quite separately from the functions performed by the equipment itself. Either method of control can be used with equipment which can perform any or all of the functions of the systems previously described. The nature of the circuitry employed in the dial system makes it possible to divide the lesson material into hundreds, even thousands, of short discrete learning units, each available to the student at any time, thus facilitating the application of the principles of programmed instruction and making maximum accommodation to individual learning rates. All normal functions of listen-record-compare are performed by dialling the proper code numbers.

On a cost basis, the dial system does not compare with systems designed to provide a relatively small number of separate programme sources. But as the need for more and more such channels becomes greater, as is already the case in experimental courses utilizing the many short lessons or 'frames' required by the application of the principles of programmed instruction (see Chapter 3, pages 21-3), the cost per available channel drops rapidly. Dial systems are not now in general use, and are custom-designed to fit individual requirements.

BOOTHS

Obviously, any of the above systems (except I) can be used with dividing partitions between the student positions, creating individual spaces or cubicles called booths. They have two functions: (1) They provide a greater sense of isolation and privacy than the student gets from headphones alone. In this connexion it must be stressed that our culture does not condone conspicuousness; many students literally dislike trying to imitate the sounds of a foreign language, which are for them unfamiliar and bizarre noises. They do not wish to appear ridiculous in the eyes (or ears) of their classmates, out of the same cultural influences which drive them to dress alike, and, indeed, to use the same speech forms in their native language. The booth at least shields them from direct observation. (2) They provide some noise cancellation by means of acoustical treatment, especially desirable when 'live' student microphones are used, as in audio-active systems III, IV and V. For a discussion of the acoustical and other factors involved, see Chapter 5, pages 92-3.

Their chief limitations are two: (1) They limit the usefulness of the room as a regular classroom. Attempts to provide adjustable or folding front or side walls sometimes involve a cost greater than the results warrant. (2) They limit the direct visual access to the student, thus restricting teacher control for disciplinary purposes. Transparent front walls, usually of glass or plexiglas, help in this respect, although direct visual access is limited to one direction.

VISUAL AIDS

Visual aids requiring equipment for presentation are films, film-strips and slides. They are mentioned here because the necessary equipment is frequently installed in language laboratories. Their principal pedagogical functions are: (1) they can illustrate meaning; (2) accompanied by a sound-track, they can serve as one basis for developing associations between the foreign language and pictured objects and situations, without the intervention of the mother-tongue; (3) they can present authentic background material of cultural value; (4) they seem to provide the student with tremendous motivation to increase his efforts in all the phases of foreign-language study, by bringing him closer to cultural reality.

In installing projection equipment in language laboratories, precautions must be taken to assure that the walls of the booths, if used, do not obstruct the students' vision from any relevant angle. Projectors are noisy. If permanent equipment, they should be installed in a separately enclosed booth or room, to isolate the language laboratory from the noise. In any case, the noise of a projector can be made less distracting by playing the sound-track through a channel which feeds the students' headphones.

5 Purchasing a Language Laboratory: General and Specific Technical Specifications

THE ALL-IMPORTANT COMMODITY

Let us assume that full consideration has been given to questions concerning teaching objectives, teaching methods, teaching materials, and teacher preparation, and that application of the criteria described in Chapter 2 has led to the choice of a specific language laboratory system. *The one technically-based commodity which the chosen system must supply, and continue to supply, is the high-quality recording and reproduction of speech.* If this is not achieved, all previous planning will have been in vain. This chapter will attempt to define high-quality speech reproduction in the specific framework of foreign-language teaching and learning, discuss the technical factors which affect its achievement, and develop the technical specifications which equipment must meet to assure that the performance of the system will conform to the standard implicit in a satisfactory statement of the requirements.

TECHNICAL LANGUAGE

Readers with many different problems and backgrounds will be interested in this chapter. Language teachers may wish some technical orientation in a strange field. Administrators and purchasing agents will want a simple statement of recommended specifications, and may be less concerned about the technical considerations underlying them. Manufacturers and design engineers will demand to know the rationale behind any such set of specifications. The language of this chapter therefore varies in technical difficulty. It is suggested that the chapter be read through once fairly rapidly. Sections of particular interest, if found difficult to follow, may be marked for more careful subsequent study. Other sections may be omitted entirely, if found too technical or not of direct interest to the particular reader.

PROCUREMENT

Since this chapter will try to develop a sound rationale for the performance requirements to be recommended, the discussion must include explanatory language not required in a simple listing of specifications. *For the convenience of administrators and purchasing personnel, therefore, major recommendations, as well as certain general provisions not specifically discussed in the guidebook, have been summarized in the form of a sample procurement specification for a typical language laboratory system. This summary appears as Appendix A, beginning on page 105.*

THE ADMINISTRATION OF SPECIFICATIONS FOR HIGH-QUALITY SOUND

The term 'high quality', as applied to sound, has only a relative meaning, as it has in many other fields. High-quality cars, shoes, or language laboratories are high in quality only in relation to other similar commodities of alleged lesser quality. For most consumer products there is a hierarchy of features or advantages which are available at a cost roughly commensurate with the number of such advantages or features, the quality of the component materials, and the costs of production and distribution. Competitive business being what it is, the consumer is accustomed to being offered both allegedly high quality and a multiplicity of features at a cost lower than that of a competitor.

The field of high-fidelity sound offers an example which will bring us closer to the special field which concerns us here. The term 'high fidelity' is regularly applied to packaged one-piece record-players retailing for £30 or less; it is also applied to carefully engineered component systems costing hundreds of pounds, with graded price differentials covering the entire area in between these extremes.

Most manufacturers try to deliver a quality product despite competitive pressures. But because of the nature of the commodity being sold, it is easy for these competitive pressures to cause hedging on specifications, especially when it is known that it is extremely difficult for the consumer to check the performance of the delivered system in such a way as to *prove* that specifications have not been met. *It cannot be overstressed that adequate sound reproduction for foreign-language instruction requires a quality standard second only to that of high-fidelity professional recording and reproducing equipment, much higher than that needed in applications whose primary requirement is the intelligible reproduction of native-language speech.* Failure to meet language laboratory specifications which set these higher quality standards can have even more far-reaching consequences than the obvious ones of inadequate sound and frequent breakdowns. The validity and effectiveness of an entire instructional programme can be endangered, and it is but an easy step to the unwarranted assumption that inadequate *hardware* is the same thing as inadequate *method*. The seeds of this confusion have already been sown.

A two-part programme, which could eventually lead to a solution, should be given every consideration:

(1) Widespread public acknowledgement by school administrators and manufacturers:

(a) that quality of sound is the prime technical consideration in the purchase of language laboratories;

(b) that specifications which guarantee this quality cannot be readily checked objectively by the consumer;

(c) that requests for estimates should be confined to those manufacturers for whose products the foreign-language teaching staff has expressed a preference on the basis of preparatory study;

(d) that part of this preparatory study should be devoted to learning how to evaluate quality sound by ear;

(e) that the choices of local staff should be based on observations of complete laboratories in operation in the field, including evaluation of sound quality.

(2) In the best interests of the school, the foreign-language teaching profession, and the manufacturer, ways should be sought to establish independent, neutral sponsorship of the kinds of instrumental testing and measurement which would guarantee that published equipment specifications would be meaningfully stated and actually met, including *component* testing under laboratory conditions, and *system* testing in the field.

WHAT MUST BE SPECIFIED?

If a recording and reproducing system made absolutely no changes in the live sound, there would be no need for electronic specifications. No such perfect system exists, however. A set of specifications, then, must include quantitative statements of how, in a given application, recorded or reproduced sound may be permitted to depart in certain ways from the original 'live' sound.

Frequency response

Sound consists of air vibrations or pulses, called sound waves, which are set in motion by some vibrating source, such as a violin string, or the human vocal cords. A simple or pure tone, like that of a tuning fork, is caused by a certain number of vibrations per second. The number, or *frequency*, of these simple vibrations determines what is perceived as the pitch of the note. Generally speaking, a low pitch is said to be low in frequency, a high pitch, high in frequency. The frequency of a tuning fork used in tuning a piano (Concert A) is 440 vibrations or *cycles per second* (cps). Complex sounds, like that of many musical instruments or the human voice, consist of vibrations at many different frequencies at once. The lowest component of these frequencies is called the *fundamental*, higher components, multiples of the fundamental, are called *harmonics*.[1]

The *frequency range* of human hearing extends, on the average, from about 16 cps to 16,000 cps, and many individuals can hear somewhat higher-frequency sounds. Some part, perhaps all, of this range is required for the faithful recording and reproduction of music, some lesser part for speech. Our first task will be to determine what part of this frequency range is required for the proper recording and reproduction of speech for foreign-language instruction. Whatever we determine will become the required *frequency response* of a language laboratory system.

It will not be sufficient simply to specify the frequency response of a language laboratory system or component. Various factors may adversely affect sound quality over whatever frequency range may be prescribed. Two important factors which require description here are *distortion* and *noise*. Excessive amounts of either can obliterate significant linguistic features. Distortion and noise can also be sources of distraction and fatigue which can seriously reduce the learning efficiency of the student.

---

[1] Musical *timbre*, e.g. the difference in perceived quality between a trombone middle C and a violin middle C, can be defined by the relative strength of different harmonics of the fundamental; the distinctive character of speech versus music is partly defined acoustically by the concentration of relatively large amounts of harmonic energy into bands of frequencies called *vowel formants*, and the relationship of these formants to each other. For a more detailed discussion, see Martin Joos, *Acoustic Phonetics*, Language Monograph 23 (Baltimore, 1948), Chapter 2, especially page 46.

Distortion

It is customary to define three types of distortion which are present in measurable quantities in all recording and reproducing systems: (1) *frequency distortion*; (2) *harmonic distortion*; (3) *intermodulation distortion*. To define frequency distortion, let us assume that a pure tone of constant intensity is introduced into a reproducing system, and then varied in frequency throughout the range the system is designed to reproduce. The intensity of the reproduced tone can be measured at various points as the tone is varied. If the intensity of the reproduced tone remains constant regardless of frequency, the response of the system is said to be *flat*; if the intensity varies at different points throughout the range, frequency distortion is said to exist. The effect of severe frequency distortion is to cause some sounds to appear much louder or weaker than others in a way which does not correspond to loudness or softness in the original sound. As will be shown later, excessive frequency distortion can also cause the difference between certain sounds to be obliterated, and cause other changes as well. *It can readily be seen that any statement of required frequency response is meaningless unless accompanied by a statement of variation in intensity over the prescribed range, expressed in decibels (db)[1] up or down (plus or minus, written ±) from some reference point, usually 1,000 cps. In this case, the smaller the decibel number, the smaller the variation, and the better the system or component.* This is shown graphically in Fig. 5.1. In this guidebook the terms 'frequency distortion' and 'intensity variation' will be used interchangeably.

The amount of *harmonic distortion* must also be specified. This is the name given to unwanted harmonics which can appear in recorded or reproduced sound, and may be said to include the spurious sum-and-difference frequencies generated when harmonics of the wanted frequencies mix with one another. Excessive amounts of harmonic distortion are caused by poor design, malfunction, or maladjustment of equipment. If the total harmonic distortion is low, *intermodulation distortion* will usually be low as well, but since there are instances when this is not true, it should also be specified. Intermodulation distortion is created by the modification of some relatively high frequency by a lower one.

Both harmonic and intermodulation distortion are expressed as a percentage.

---

[1] All measurements in decibels are similarly meaningless unless the reference point or reference level is known.

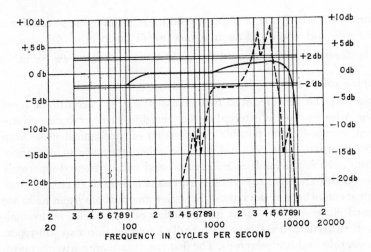

Fig. 5.1.

Chart showing measurement of frequency response. Differences in intensity are shown along the vertical axis in decibels up and down from zero db, the intensity at 1,000 cps. Frequency in cps is shown on the horizontal scale. Note that zero db does not mean that there is no intensity at 1,000 cps; whatever the intensity at 1,000 cps may be, it is taken as a reference point from which deviations are measured. The horizontal reference lines mark the limits of the area of variation of plus or minus 2 db. The solid curved line shows the response of a system which is nearly flat: 100-8,000 cps±2 db, ref. 1,000 cps, read as one hundred to eight thousand cycles per second, plus or minus two decibels, with one thousand cycles per second as reference point. The dotted curve shows a very different response, quite unsatisfactory for language laboratories. It is down 20 db at 400 cps, rises steeply and erratically to 1,000 cps, flattens off briefly, and is characterized by many other irregularities in the range above 1,000 cps.

Wow and flutter

Wow and flutter are periodic variations in the reproduced sound generally caused by mechanical imperfections in tape recorders and record-players, and must be specified for these components. Both are also measured as a percentage. The effect of wow is well known to anyone who has heard a record-player operating erratically, causing the pitch of recorded music to vary in a most annoying manner. Flutter is more subtle, but is simply a more rapid periodic variation than wow. A bad case of flutter would make a flute note sound like a bird trill, and would put an annoying burble on speech.

In all percentage measurements, the smaller the figure the better the system.[1]

Types of noise

Noise may be classified into two general types: (1) acoustic or room noise, whose source is external to the recording or reproducing equipment, except for the possible contribution of mechanical noise from tape recorders, switches, and the like, when they are in operation. Room noise is amenable to *noise control*, and will be treated separately later in this chapter; (2) *system noise*, characteristic of electronic components anywhere in the system. Excessive amounts of system noise are caused either by limitations in the design of equipment, or by malfunction. System noise may be broadly classified into two sub-types: *inherent noise* and *extraneous noise*. The first requires quantitative measurement to ensure satisfactory performance, the second does not.

Inherent noise and signal-to-noise ratio

All recording and reproducing systems have some inherent noise in them. It is an important characteristic of amplifiers, for example, and of tape recording circuitry. Since such noise, caused for the most part by disturbances within the electronic parts and circuits themselves, can never be entirely eliminated, what is important is the relationship of the intensity of the inherent noise in a system to the intensity of the sound one wishes to hear. As defined in the glossary of Chapter 1, the sound one wishes to hear is called the *signal*. Another very important measurement of system performance, then, is the *signal-to-noise ratio*, stated in decibels below a reference power level. *The larger the decibel number, the better the signal-to-noise ratio.*

Extraneous noise

Either through poor design, poor installation, or malfunction, extraneous noise can be introduced into a system. These kinds of noise must be described so that they can be identified, but, as stated above, it will not be necessary to give actual quantitative specifications, since for all practical purposes extraneous noise should be inaudible at normal listening level. Typical extraneous noises are: *hum*, a steady tone of low or medium pitch which is present whenever the equipment is

---

[1] Except the sound-absorption coefficient of acoustic materials—see pp. 91-2.

turned on, and may or may not increase with changes in the volume setting; various kinds of static-like noises, called by technicians, according to the probable source, *frying*, or *grid whine*; a squealing sound, called *feedback*, which should not occur under normal operating conditions;[1] a metallic ringing or echoing sound, accentuated when the equipment is moved or jarred, called *microphonics*; the presence of an unwanted voice or voices in the background of the programme, called *crosstalk*. There can also be pops or clicks made by throwing switches anywhere in the system. It is not uncommon for two or more of these noise types to produce an annoying jumble of extraneous noise in the background of the recorded voice. Both inherent and extraneous noise can produce an effect called *masking*, which can make it extremely difficult for the foreign-language learner to distinguish certain sounds.

FREQUENCY RESPONSE, DISTORTION AND NOISE: VIEWS AND VIEWPOINTS

Many different views have been expressed, mostly informally, concerning the audio characteristics which language laboratory equipment should possess. These views stem from the different viewpoints imposed by various special fields and research activities seldom directly concerned with our problem. The relevance of the views of a particular specialist is not always clear. Much confusion exists, and informal expressions of opinion concerning desirable characteristics range from 300-3,000 cps, at relatively high distortion and noise levels, to 50-15,000 cps, with correspondingly low levels of distortion and noise, to state the two extreme positions. It is the purpose of this section to examine the viewpoints of various fields, and to discuss both their limitations and their significance in the special field which concerns us here.

Telephone circuitry and intelligibility studies; the problem of underspecification
It has long been recognized that satisfactory intelligibility for native-language speech is achieved by telephone circuitry and apparatus whose frequency response is roughly 300-3,000 cps.[2] Deviations in

---

[1] A live microphone held directly in front of a live headphone or loudspeaker will practically always produce feedback.

[2] Harvey Fletcher, *Speech and Hearing in Communication* (New York: D. Van Nostrand Company, 1953), Chapter 16. See also W. F. Tuffnell, '500-type Telephone Set', *Bell Telephone Record* (September, 1951), 414-18.

intensity over this range (see pages 44-5) are not normally considered important in this application. Further, intelligibility studies, stimulated and supported by various sources, including military services properly concerned with the need to communicate by voice under high noise conditions, have indicated that this range can be deteriorated by various kinds of noise and distortion to a degree far exceeding what would be encountered in recording and reproducing equipment of the most primitive design, and still preserve intelligibility for the purposes of communication. *It is most important to understand that the 'intelligibility' factor measured by such studies is largely irrelevant to the design of systems to be used for foreign-language instruction.* The reasons why this is so will be explained. The point is stressed only because many electronics design engineers, while admitting that there seem to be other factors involved, are psychologically influenced in the direction of conceptions based on such studies of intelligibility, especially as applied to telephone circuitry. Resulting design compromises are frequently unconsciously supported by the reservation that, after all, it's only speech, and the requirements for satisfactory speech intelligibility are relatively low, and easy to achieve.

Redundancy as a factor in intelligibility. To understand why intelligibility studies are largely irrelevant in the present context one must be aware of certain properties of every language which operate only if the listener is a native speaker of that language. Every language has the property called *redundancy*. As used in everyday language, this word means saying more than is strictly necessary. Teachers of English composition may criticize a student for saying *a typical type* when *type* alone would suffice. As a technical term, the word means much the same thing. It is not, however, something undesirable, but rather a definite property of language capable, in fact, of being expressed quantitatively. Cover the bottom half of a line of type with a card; the line can usually still be read. The lower half of each letter may be said to be redundant. In speech, in the sentence, 'This man's nxxx is John', where the x's stand for sounds imperfectly heard, there is not much doubt that the obscure word is *name*. Everyone has had the experience of successfully—even if with some difficulty—carrying on a conversation at a noisy party or in the presence of noisy construction work. It is the built-in redundancy of language which makes this possible. In short, we rely on many different simultaneous and successive cues to extract meaning from a native language sentence; many of them can be eliminated by room noise, or by noise and distortion in an electronic reproducing system, and the meaning will still be understood.

That some of the cues thus eliminated in the usual telephone system are essential to full intelligibility even in the native language is evident from the fact that we always spell unfamiliar words or proper names over the telephone; the telephone operator uses a phonetic alphabet to distinguish *b* and *v* and *d*, saying: 'Was that *b* as in *boy*, *v* as in *Victor*, or *d* as in *dog*?' It is evident, then, that the native speaker makes full use of the redundancy of language when listening under any conditions of limited frequency response, noise or distortion. *It is equally evident that none of the redundancy available in the native language is available to the beginning student of a foreign language.* It is completely unintelligible to him, either live, or reproduced over a system of even the highest attainable fidelity.[1] He needs to hear as much as possible or practical of the linguistic data in the speech wave, if he is to learn to distinguish the sounds of the foreign language from similar sounds in the foreign language, and from similar sounds in his own language which he tends to substitute for them. Only in this way, after he has also acquired other equally important dimensions of the new language, can the redundancy of the foreign language eventually offer him the multiplicity of meaning cues with which the native speaker operates. It will be shown that adequate reproduction of the data needed by the student to accomplish this requires a frequency range, a flatness of response, and distortion and noise requirements far exceeding that of telephone equipment.

The problem of overspecification

The opinions of linguists and language teachers who understand the considerations just discussed, have tended in the opposite direction. As previously stated, informal recommendations of a frequency response of 50-15,000 cps, with appropriately stringent distortion and noise requirements, are not uncommon. The cost of such equipment is high, but if it could be conclusively demonstrated that such performance is

---

[1] See Ilse Lehiste and Gordon E. Peterson, 'Linguistic considerations in the study of speech intelligibility', *Journal of the Acoustical Society of America*, 31/3 (March, 1959), 280-6.

required in language-laboratory applications, cost alone could not be considered a valid objection. But, while this guidebook must repeatedly stress that much higher performance characteristics are required than are frequently found in actual installations, and certainly much higher than those required for native-language intelligibility, it simply cannot be demonstrated that such extremes of frequency response are required. Indeed, some authorities feel that such an extended range would be undesirable (see pages 57, 63-4, 67-8). This tendency to overspecify is based not on exhaustive examination of the evidence, but on tactical considerations which, it will be shown, have their own peculiar validity.

Intuitively aware of the engineer's reservations with respect to speech requirements, the linguist and language teacher have come to feel that if specifications are made very high, they may at least get something better than would have been the case if the specifications had been lower. This point of view is not entirely without justification, especially in view of the difficulties in administering specifications, already discussed at the beginning of this chapter. Specifically, they fear that less demanding statements about frequency response, distortion and noise will not only give free rein to the tendency of the engineer to think in terms of alleged lesser requirements for speech, but also encourage the quite unwarranted transfer of this tendency to other aspects of design, such as proper operating conditions of circuit components, and precautions to help assure long life and trouble-free operation. The requirements for speech reproduction are often associated with the cheapest kind of intercom equipment. The foreign-language professional will continue to have a basis for concern as long as instances of such confusion on the part of manufacturers and engineers exist. The tendency to conceal poor design and poor quality components beneath the glitter of complicated gadgetry must also be deplored. The language field needs better sound and fewer flashing lights.

Psycholinguistic implications of linguistic theory

The field of *descriptive linguistics* describes language, the system of vocal symbols by means of which people communicate. *Psycholinguistics* studies the relationships between language and the people who produce it and respond to it. When the linguist makes informal recommendations concerning frequency response and other specifications for language laboratories, he is not usually drawing upon linguistic theory, but on his knowledge of acoustic phonetics, which will be discussed in the next section. His views may be influenced in certain ways, however, by his knowledge of linguistic theory, and by certain implications of that body of theory for psycholinguistics. Let us briefly review these theories and these implications.

As a small child gradually acquires his native language, he learns to attach importance to differences among sounds which make differences in meaning, and to ignore all others. There are, thus, many objectively different sounds which the native speaker comes to regard as 'the same thing'. It is hard, for example, to convince a native speaker of English that the aspirated *t*-sound in the word *tick* is very different from the unaspirated *t*-sound in the word *stick*, yet this difference is great enough so that in other languages, Chinese, for example, these two sounds are distinctive, and words can be distinguished in meaning by these differences.

The similar, but objectively different, non-distinctive sounds in a given language are what the linguist calls *allophones*; a class of such similar variants (allophones) is what the linguist calls a *phoneme*. Certain allophones are said to be in free variation, for example, the final *t*-sound in *hat* may be exploded with a strong puff of breath, or may be 'unreleased', i.e. the tongue-tip stays at the front of the roof of the mouth. The native speaker of American English will perceive both pronunciations as the word *hat*, but will tend to associate the former with 'British English', or with a markedly formal style. Other allophonic differences are *conditioned* by neighbouring sounds. Thus, an unaspirated *t* is always heard after *s*, as in the word *stick* used as an example above. Such conditioned allophones of the same phoneme are almost always perceived as 'sames' by a native speaker, yet he always makes the proper objective differences when he speaks, and is immediately aware that a foreigner has done something peculiar if the latter treats them differently. It is the mismanagement of allophonic differences which accounts for much of what we call a foreign accent.

The notion of allophonic differences is valid only within a given language. But the foreign-language learner will tend to group 'allophones' into 'phonemes' in the new language *as they are grouped in his native language*. He will thus tend to hear differences within the new language which the native speaker does not regard as significant, and to ignore others to which the native speaker attaches great importance. In a certain sense it may be said, then, that a foreign-language learner is partially deaf to the new sounds and new contrasts which he finds in the foreign language, not physically deaf, of course, assuming that there is nothing wrong with his hearing, but perceptually deaf.[1]

This notion of perceptual deafness to new sounds and new contrasts in the foreign language, and to the differences between these and similar sounds in the native language certainly reinforces the statement that all the relevant data in the sound waves must be preserved. Even when they are indeed present, the student can have difficulty perceiving them.

There are other implications, particularly for equipment design. It might very well be possible that the exact data in the sound waves which contain the information that the student persists in ignoring because he is a native speaker of a different language could be stressed or enhanced by controlled modifications of these data intentionally introduced into the reproducing system. It is known, for example, that extra amplification of middle frequencies in music seems to add a certain kind of liveness or presence to the reproduction.[2] In motion-picture sound-track recording, the frequencies above 1,000 cps are accentuated to add presence to the voice.[3] There is also some slender evidence from the field of speech therapy. A rather unexpectedly wide frequency response seems to be required to bring a speech defect forcefully to the attention of a patient.[4]

When we talk, we hear ourselves as we speak. This 'self-monitoring' seems to be essential for normal speech. If the ability to monitor oneself is disturbed, speech deteriorates. Such disturbances of the 'simultaneous feedback' which controls the smooth flow of speech may be caused by disease, or by neurological abnormalities, or may be experi-

---

[1] The idea of perceptual deafness, which is related to what the psychologist calls *acquired similarity* vs. *acquired distinctiveness*, is developed here on linguistic grounds. It has received some experimental corroboration in certain studies in speech perception. See Liberman, Harris, Hoffman and Griffith, 'The discrimination of speech sounds within and across phoneme boundaries', *Journal of Experimental Psychology*, 54/5 (November, 1957); and Lotz, Abramson, Gerstman, Ingemann and Nemser, 'The perception of English stops by speakers of English, Spanish, Hungarian and Thai: A tape-cutting experiment', *Language and Speech*, 3/2 (April-June, 1960).

[2] See also A. S. Hayes, 'Problems of the language laboratory', *Monograph Series on Linguistics and Language Teaching*, 2 (Georgetown University Press, September, 1952).

[3] H. Tremaine, *The Audio Cyclopedia* (Indianapolis, Indiana: Howard W. Sams & Co., Inc., 1959), 617.

[4] C. J. LeBel, 'Standards for educational recording machines', *Quarterly Journal of Speech*, 36 (December, 1950), 520-3.

mentally induced by a special head arrangement on a tape recorder, in which case we speak of 'delayed feedback.'[1] It is thus definitely possible to change how a subject or a student will speak, by controlling how he hears himself. It follows that it might be possible, in an audio-active system, to *enhance* a student's ability to imitate, by using special adjustable filters in the circuitry which feeds his headphones, so that he would hear the voice of the speaker on the tape exactly as it was recorded, but would hear his own voice, as he repeated, modified by the filters.[2]

We must conclude, then, that convincing experimental evidence of the merits of modifying the audio characteristics either of what the model says, or of what the learner hears himself repeat, is almost wholly lacking in the context of foreign-language teaching. These are, however, extremely promising research areas, which might eventually drastically affect specifications for language laboratories. But, at the present writing, these possibilities cannot be taken into account.

Acoustic phonetics

Acoustic phonetics is the branch of linguistic science which studies and classifies the raw data of speech from an acoustic point of view, analysing the sound waves themselves. Its orientation is thus different from *articulatory phonetics*, which describes speech sounds in terms of the positions and movements of the organs of speech (tongue, lips, etc.) which are required to produce them. An important tool used in acoustic phonetics, and in the special area in psycholinguistics which studies the perception of speech, is the sound *spectrograph*, which despite certain limitations, will be directly useful in determining frequency-response specifications. This device shows the harmonic structure of a segment of speech. It also shows the relative distribution of energy throughout the frequency range, which is responsible for the differences among many sounds, and the special properties of the transitions from one segment of speech to another, which are responsible for other differences. Physically, the recording, called a *spectrogram*, appears as bands of varying shades of grey on special paper. The height of the recording corresponds to frequency, the width, to time. The varying

---

[1] There is a considerable literature. See R. A. Chase *et al.*, 'Bibliography: delayed audio feedback', *Journal of Speech and Hearing Research*, 2 (1959), 193-200.

[2] See P. R. Leon, *Laboratoire de Langues et Correction Phonétique* (Paris, Didier, 1962), 213-15.

shades of grey correspond to differences in the amount of energy present at different bands of frequencies. The spectrogram itself, or information taken from spectrograms plotted in various ways, may be called a *spectrum*.

Studies in speech perception using speech synthesis

Psycholinguistic research dealing with speech perception seeks to isolate the acoustic cues which a listener uses to discriminate sounds.

Using sound spectrograms, it is possible to isolate certain characteristics of this record which are tentatively considered to correspond to essential cues in the sound waves. Simplified spectrograms displaying these same features are then made by hand and played back by means of a complex device called a pattern playback. The result is synthetic or artificial speech. It is then possible to make small variations in the features represented on a handmade spectrogram and note the reactions of a native speaker on hearing it played back. By this means one can pinpoint precisely those acoustic features which the listener uses to distinguish sounds.[1] Studies in speech perception based on speech synthesis will be helpful wherever the redundancy available to the native speaker has been eliminated by the choice of items to be evaluated. Few such studies, however, have been directly concerned with the perceptual problems of foreign-language students.[2]

'Learning' experiments

On the surface, it would seem that the frequency range required for optimum foreign-language learning could readily be established by setting up a 'learning' situation, and noting variations in learning

---

[1] Many linguists view the sound system of a language not so much as a 'set of sounds', but rather as a *network of differences between sounds*. In this frame of reference, the elements of such a sound system cannot be defined positively in terms of what they 'are', but only negatively in terms of what they are not, i.e. what they contrast with. This view will necessarily question some of the basic assumptions of speech perception studies based on spectrographic manipulations. For a good discussion, see C. F. Hockett, *A Course in Modern Linguistics* (New York, Macmillan, 1958), 24-6, 112-19.

[2] See the articles by Liberman *et al.*, op. cit., and Lotz *et al.*, op. cit. Also research in progress: Pierre Delattre, 'Research on general phonetic characteristics of languages', University of Colorado, Boulder, Colorado; and Harlan Lane, 'Experimental analysis of the control of speech production and perception', University of Michigan, Ann Arbor, Michigan. Both of these investigations are being performed pursuant to contracts between the respective universities and the U.S. Office of Education.

efficiency as high and low frequency cut-off points are altered. Very few such experiments have even been attempted. They are extremely difficult to design, administer, and analyse, because of the many variables which must be controlled to ensure that the results will be unambiguous. One recently performed experiment,[1] investigating the effects of high-frequency cut-off, shows quite clearly that a cut-off at 3,000 cps seriously inhibited perception of certain consonant sounds in German. German has a number of significant contrasts among the fricative sounds, which contain a good deal of high-frequency energy. French, on the other hand, which has fewer such contrasts, seemed resistant to the effects of high-frequency cut-off, although there were, indeed, differences in the effects of the two lower cut-off points, 3,000 and 5,000 cps respectively. In German, the 5,000 cps cut-off yielded much better results than did the 3,000 cps cut-off. The still better performance yielded by a cut-off of about 7,300 cycles was, however, not statistically significant when compared with the results achieved with a 5,000 cps cut-off.

It is at this point that some limitations of the experiment itself come into question. Such experiments, like the language laboratory itself, are seriously inhibited by the current lack of headphones whose performance approaches that readily attainable in other parts of the reproducing system, a problem to be discussed in detail below. This problem is frankly acknowledged in the report of this experiment.

Pairs of words, differing in one important sound, were heard by the student, followed by a pause in which he was to repeat the pair. This repetition was recorded for subsequent analysis, which would try to determine the effects of the various high-frequency cut-offs on *mimicry*, as opposed to *discrimination*. Analysis of the effects of both low-frequency and high-frequency restriction on mimicry are discussed by Freeman and Buka in a later report (see footnote, Chapter 5, page 57). Results are suggestive but largely inconclusive.

After the repetition pause, one of the words of the pair was repeated, and the student indicated on an answer sheet which word he thought

---

[1] M. Buka, M. Z. Freeman, W. N. Locke, 'Language learning and frequency response', in E. W. Najam, Ed., *Methods and Materials for the Language Laboratory*, Publication 18, Indiana University Research Center in Anthropology, Folklore, and Linguistics. Supplement to *International Journal of American Linguistics*, 28/1 (January, 1962). The experimentation described in this article was supported by a grant from Educational Facilities Laboratories, Inc.

had been repeated, the first or the second. This is known as a 'matching' or 'ABX' procedure. It seems apparent that the 3,000 cps cut-off obliterated certain important contrasts for many students. But it is quite possible that the pairs he was hearing with the 5,000 cps cut-off were now sufficiently different to enable him to *match* more successfully, since matching requires only that the student remember a difference, in fact, *any* difference. As one adds more high frequencies, the differences become greater, but not enough greater to be statistically significant, since there is now always some difference between the pairs. In short, the technique can demonstrate when significant contrasts are *obliterated*, but not at what point the quality of the reproduction provides an accurate model.

FREQUENCY RESPONSE AND INTENSITY VARIATION: A FRESH ANALYSIS[1]

Let us now attempt to arrive at the needed specifications by examining the whole sound spectrum, to see where the speech data of interest are located. Some things are definitely known and others are disputed or imperfectly understood. The results of this examination of the data will yield one or more statements of desirable total-system response. These statements will then have to be qualified in certain ways, taking into consideration what is possible and practical at the present state of the art, as well as intelligent planning for the future.

The total frequency range can be divided into three subdivisions: (1) the low end, from 60 to 250 cps; (2) the middle range, from 250 to 6,000 cps; (3) the top end, from 6,000 cps upward.

The low end (60-250 cps)

Even though minimal phonetic cues do not begin to appear until about 150 cps and really significant markers can scarcely be said to exist until about 200-250 cps, it could be argued that an ideal system should reproduce the lowest fundamental frequency of a man's voice, which

---

[1] A number of scholars have contributed in significant ways, in discussion, correspondence, and in their publications, to the treatment of these problems which follows, including Professor Pierre Delattre, of the University of Colorado, Professor Morris Halle, of the Massachusetts Institute of Technology, and Professor Martin Joos of the University of Wisconsin. The writer, however, assumes all responsibility for the present synthesis of available data and prevailing, sometimes contradictory, opinions, as well as for any inaccuracies which may be found here or elsewhere in this presentation.

can go down as low as 60 cps. But there are good reasons for attenuating (reducing) certain lower frequencies in any system designed for the reproduction of speech, although the reasons may differ in different applications. It is known that low frequencies, generally speaking, have a tendency to mask higher frequencies if the intensity of the lower tone is high enough.[1] It is simplest to consider this problem from the point of view of reproducing a live voice by means of a professional microphone and amplifier, uncomplicated by tape recording, so that the signal presented to the headphones is substantially flat in the 60 to 250 cps region. Although a large part of speech power is concentrated in the 250-500 cps range,[2] there can be sufficient power in the low-end frequencies to cause serious masking of important higher frequencies under the special conditions of extremely close coupling to the ear. Such close coupling is normal when headphones are used, and is indeed recommended on other grounds.[3] Many male voices and certain types of female voices characterized by an extremely husky or alto quality can make it difficult to distinguish important consonant markers at all, without considerable listening to make the necessary perceptual adjustments. If the volume is simply turned down, important higher frequencies may be reduced to inaudibility. Then, too, much room noise is at low-end frequencies, and extremes of low-frequency response can increase the difficulty of adjusting both intercom and audio-active facilities.

Some of these frequencies, however, do contribute to naturalness of reproduction. A compromise response is indicated which reduces extremes of energy in this region, yet preserves enough to assure natural sounding speech. This can be achieved by a response which rises from about -15 db at 120 cps to zero db at 250 cps.[4]

---

[1] Fletcher, op. cit., 154.

[2] Ibid., 78.

[3] Chiefly to provide better isolation from room noise and to assure good response below 300 cps. See 82-7, *passim*.

[4] A learning experiment using low-frequency cut-off points of 50, 500 and 1,000 cps is reported by Margaret Z. Freeman and Magda Buka, 'Language learning and frequency response II' (mimeographed). These tests continue the experimentation reported under '*Learning*' *Experiments* above, 54-6. While statistically significant results are reported in favour of the lower frequency cut-off for German (not French), the choice of cut-off frequencies permits no conclusions concerning the effect of cut-off at frequencies between 50 and 500 cps, which is precisely the problem area.

The middle range (250-6,000 cps)

Sound spectrograms indicate quite clearly that this is where most of the linguistically significant phonetic features are located: all of the vowel sounds, and most, but not all of the consonants. Two characteristics of a response curve in this region are important, both of which have thus far been subsumed under the name frequency distortion or intensity variation. Such a curve might have sudden sharp *peaks* or broad *valleys*. A peak may be defined as an area of extra amplification less than a quarter-octave wide; a valley as an area of attenuation (reduction) more than a quarter-octave wide.[1] Such peaks or valleys can seriously mar the reproduction capabilities of a system designed for foreign-language instruction. A peak, particularly in the 250-4,000 cps region, can impart a nasal quality to the reproduction, among other possibilities. In the range of 250-6,000 cps, there should be no peaks or valleys in the response curve greater than 1 db.

There might be no such peaks or valleys, yet the line running from 250 to 6,000 cps could be straight, indicating no deviations, or could slope gradually upward or downward, indicating a gradual rise or fall in intensity. A proper slope for a suitable response curve may be level, or may rise to no more than 3 db at 6,000 cps, but must not fall. A fall, particularly in the 250-4,000 cps region, can change the quality of certain vowels in a most undesirable manner, making the vowel in French *si* sound more like the vowel in *su*, or the first vowel in German *besser* sound more like the first vowel in *böse*.

The top end (from 6,000 cps upward)

This is the region in which is found energy from a number of fricative consonants, particularly sounds like *f* and *fit* and *th* in *thing*. 'At the present time, the production, the perception, and the acoustical properties of the voiceless fricative consonants are only partially understood. . . . The perception of fricatives has been studied by various methods, particularly by synthesis techniques, but our understanding of the important cues is far from complete.'[2]

Our first problem in discussing top-end characteristics will be to determine the upper frequency limits that language laboratory equip-

---

[1] A frequency an octave higher than any given frequency is twice that frequency; a frequency an octave lower than any given frequency is half that frequency.

[2] J. M. Heinz and K. N. Stevens, 'On the properties of voiceless fricative consonants', *Journal of the Acoustical Society of America*, 33/5 (May, 1961).

ment should be capable of reproducing. Certain factors have limited the usefulness of the sound spectrograph as an analytical tool for the investigation of high-frequency sounds. Until very recently, the upper frequency limit of the sound spectrograph was around 8,500 cps, more often 8,000 cps, and there is at present no published work based on spectrographic analysis using newer machines which go up to 12,000 cps. Further, as one goes up the frequency scale, the intensity of speech sounds at these higher frequencies is so much less than that of lower-frequency sounds, that adjustments have to be made to the spectrograph to make the higher-frequency sounds show up at all. It is possible to examine spectrographically sound energy higher than 8,500 cps by playing an appropriate speech sample at half speed. By this means it has been established that for most fricative sounds there is some energy present around 10,000 cps, and, in a few cases, up to 12,000 cps.[1] There has been no study of the relevance of high-frequency energy beyond 10,000 cps to the perception of speech sounds. The extreme weakness of the energy present at these frequencies, which can be missed completely by people with even moderate hearing loss, make it most unlikely that they contain any useful cues at all.[2] Some investigators, however, have suggested informally that frequencies above 10,000 cps may contribute to naturalness of speech reproduction. This possibility will be discussed in a somewhat different context, on pages 67 and 68.

Published investigations bearing upon the relevance of the high-frequency energy in speech between 8,000 and 10,000 cps have not used spectrographic analysis, because of the limitations just described. The precise details of the much more complex techniques used will not be described here.[3] These techniques yield spectra which are plottings of frequency against energy in decibels. From such spectra it has been established that, for example, the f-sound in fit or cuff, as well as the th-sound in thing, show peaks of energy in the 7,000 to 10,000 cps range. The s-sound in soothe shows peaks extending somewhat below this range, centring back in what we have called the middle range, around 5,000 cps. The sh-sound in sheep will have its peak still lower, well into

---

[1] Peter Strevens, 'Spectra of fricative noise in human speech', *Language and Speech*, 3/1 (January-March, 1960).

[2] Fletcher, op. cit., 78 and 137.

[3] G. W. Hughes and M. Halle, 'Special properties of fricative consonants', *Journal of the Acoustical Society of America*, 28/2, 303-10.

our middle range, around 2,500 cps. It is reasonably safe to assume that we will not find in any language peaks that go higher than those found in *f* or *th*.

In order to evaluate the importance of these peaks in identifying *f* and *th*, which contain the highest documented peaks, let us first examine some other kinds of evidence concerning the perception of four fricative sounds: *f*, *th* (as in *thing*), *s*, *sh*. Cues for distinguishing these sounds (and other fricatives as well) must be either in the fricative noise itself, or in the preceding or following vowel.[1] By cutting and rearranging fricative and vocalic portions of tape-recorded syllables containing these sounds, it has been convincingly demonstrated that 'the listener may be said to behave as if he first decided on the basis of friction, whether the syllable belonged to the *s-sh* class or to the *f-th* class. If *s* or *sh*, he uses the friction again to decide which of these alternatives it was. If, on the other hand, the first decision had been that the sound belonged in the *f-th* class, then the listener uses the vocalic portion to decide which of the two sounds, *f* or *th*, he had heard.'[2] These conclusions are substantiated by Heinz and Stevens.[3] It is also readily observable that if *f*-friction and *th*-friction are pronounced in random order by a live speaker, they cannot be distinguished at distances greater than a few feet (when the speaker's mouth is not visible to the listener), yet the difficulty disappears when the friction is pronounced with a following vowel.

Characteristics of the friction noise in *f*, then, are not used to distinguish it from *th*. To pursue further the relevance of the friction noise of *f* to other distinctions, we need to examine how, following Harris above, the listener does indeed decide that a given friction noise belongs to the *s-sh* class on the one hand, or to the *f-th* class on the other.

Examining the spectra of Hughes and Halle,[4] we find a bewildering variety of distributions of energy, which varies considerably from

---

[1] Vowels are identified acoustically by their *formant* structure. A formant (cf. footnote, p. 43) is a band of frequencies containing a concentration of harmonic energy, and there are several such formants associated with each vowel. Certain consonant sounds are known to be characterized, in part, by the shape of the formants in the area of transition to an adjacent vowel.

[2] K. S. Harris, 'Cues for the discrimination of American English fricatives in spoken syllables', *Language and Speech*, 1/1 (January-March, 1958), 1-7.

[3] Op. cit., 596.

[4] Op. cit., 305-7.

speaker to speaker. The f-friction seems to be characterized, in most cases, by one or more energy peaks in the 7,000-9,000 cps range, a few showing a rising characteristic at 10,000 cps, the limit of their instrumentation. There is also a broad pattern of lower-frequency noise with occasional peaks between 1,000 and 2,000 cps. The s-friction has peaks somewhat below this point, averaging around 5,000 cps; sh is still lower, averaging around 2,500 cps. That the low-frequency energy present in f is one of the important cues is evident from the results of a perceptual test based on mechanical production of fricative noise, with frequencies above 6,500 cps eliminated. A good percentage of f-responses was made to friction noise in which the low-frequency energy was at least equal to the high-frequency energy present up to 6,500 cps. When the high-frequency energy predominated (note again that the high f-peaks had been purposely eliminated), listeners made a high percentage of s-responses.[1]

Let us turn again to Heinz and Stevens.[2] Using a similar mechanical procedure, they elicited responses from listeners to fricative noise having various resonant frequencies, various intensities, and various manners of transition to a following vowel.[3] Responses of sh were always associated with a resonant frequency in the vicinity of 2,500 cps, agreeing well with Hughes and Halle. Responses of s were obtained when the resonant frequency was above 3,000 cps, and f and th responses were obtained for very high frequency resonances, *particularly when the intensity of the fricative was low*. It should also be noted that the addition of low-frequency noise, described above as an f-cue in the absence of the higher frequencies, did not significantly increase f and th responses *when the higher frequencies were present*. Unfortunately for our purposes, the noise generator used in this experiment went only as high as 8,000 cps, and it has been argued that higher frequencies would produce even better f-stimuli. But it is significant that two of the f and th stimuli used

---

[1] Note that th was not a possible response in this test, so that f-th discrimination on this basis is not involved. Note also that in such perceptual tests, there are no 'correct' responses. The listener must identify as some speech sound a synthetic noise of known acoustic characteristics. It is precisely this identification, or 'response', which is of interest.

[2] Op. cit., 595-6.

[3] It was their interpretation of the effects of the latter variable which corroborated the conclusion of Harris that the f-th distinction depends on the vocalic portion of the syllable.

by Heinz and Stevens were unanimously judged to be 'natural' syllables.

The authors (Heinz and Stevens) properly advise caution in interpreting data based on responses to stimuli having a resonant frequency of 8,000 cps, because the laboratory-standard headphones used can show fluctuations as great as 8 db in the range 7,000-9,000 cps. An examination of independently made curves of the response of a sample of these phones corroborates this statement, and indicates that the deviation at 8,000 cps was probably in the minus direction. Since the response of these headphones at 2,500 cps, the lowest of the resonant frequencies used, is about +2 db from the reference point of 1,000 cps, the actual pertinent deviation was probably −10 db at 8,000 cps, although there could be considerable variation from phone to phone. Responses of *f* were clearly better at 8,000 cps than at 6,500 cps, *at low intensities* which were measured without reference to the headphones. The drop in response at this frequency due to the headphones would have the effect of reducing further the intensity of the signal heard by the subjects relative to the vocalic portion of the syllable, and thereby, again in the light of the better *f*-responses achieved at 8,000 cps, reinforce the conclusion that both low intensity and high frequency can be distinctive cues for *f* versus *s* or *sh*.

It could have been argued immediately that, since there are clearly high-frequency peaks of energy in *f*, the frequency range of language-laboratory equipment should certainly include them, but it was felt to be necessary to show that these peaks are indeed used, at least some of the time, by native speakers to discriminate *f* from *s* and *sh*. The reason why native speakers appear to use different cues under different circumstances is again to be found in the concept of redundancy, extended to their reactions to different energy and intensity distributions within the fricative consonants, not only as simulated by mechanical means for testing purposes, but as actually found in the speech of different speakers. It is known, for example, that there can be wide departures from a hypothetical 'normal' position of the speech organs in producing a given sound, which nevertheless produce the 'same' result acoustically.[1] It is inviting to suppose that the converse of this is true on the perceptual level. In the case of the fricatives, various combinations of energy distribution, taken with various relative intensities, can elicit

---

[1] Francis J. Carmody, 'X-ray studies of speech articulation', *University of California Publications in Modern Philology*, 20/4 (1937).

the same response. But for the foreign language learner, the high-frequency cues must be present, since we want to present him with all the data which are ever used in discriminating among the fricative sounds.

It is now clear that language laboratory equipment should be capable of reproducing the high-frequency peaks found in the fricative sounds *f* and *th*. Since practical systems do not reproduce up to some frequency and cut off abruptly, it is necessary to establish up to just what point in this range reasonably flat response is desirable, and beyond which the response may be permitted to fall rapidly to some higher frequency, which will then be considered a nominal cut-off point. We know that the precise location of peaks of high-frequency energy in *f* varies considerably among different speakers. Again using the spectra of Hughes and Halle, we find that the arithmetical average of all high *f*-peaks is just under 8,500 cps. If we bear in mind that certain *f*-stimuli at 8,000 cps, plus vowel, were unanimously judged by the Heinz and Stevens subjects to be 'natural' syllables, and remember that the possibility of achieving better *f*-discrimination by the inclusion of still higher frequencies has not been experimentally determined, it seems that flat response to 8,500 cps should provide an adequate safety factor. Intensity variations between 6,000 and 8,500 cps should not be troublesome if no greater than ± 5 db.

It has been pointed out that practical systems do not reproduce up to some stated frequency and cut off abruptly. Some authorities have also stated that the range above 10,000 cps can contribute disturbing squeaks, paper rustling, and the like, indicating that these frequencies are best eliminated entirely. We have set 8,500 cps as the top-end point up to which an ideal system should have reasonably flat frequency response. It is impractical on cost grounds to design cut-off facilities sharp enough to assure flat response at 8,500 cps and virtual cut-off (20 to 25 db down) at 10,000 cps. It is, therefore, recommended that frequencies above 8,500 cps be attenuated as rapidly as consistent with economical design. In practice, considerable attenuation in this region is likely to be contributed by the recording and reproducing heads used in tape-recording equipment.

To recapitulate: The response requirement thus delineated for language laboratory systems should be as follows:

          120 cps — —15 db
          250 cps —   0 db

250-6,000 cps —   ±2 db, slope flat or slightly rising, no peaks or
                               valleys greater than 1 db
6,000-8,500 cps —   ±5 db
     8,500 cps up, rapid attenuation
These response data are plotted as a curve in Fig. 5.2.

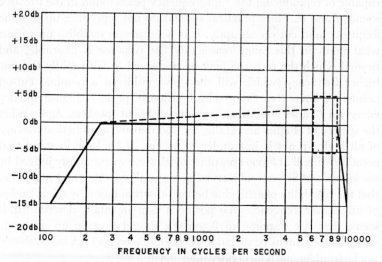

FREQUENCY IN CYCLES PER SECOND

Fig. 5.2. Ideal Frequency Response Curve for Language-Laboratory
Systems.

See pp. 63-4. The broken line shows the permitted 3 db slope from 250-6,000 cps.
The intensity within this range may vary ±2 db, but such deviation from flat
response should not produce sharp peaks or broad valleys, as defined on p. 58.
The area boxed in by broken lines is the 6,000-8,500 cps area, within which
deviations no greater than ±5 db may be tolerated. The attenuation shown
above 8,500 cps is more rapid than is actually practical.

The response curve shown in Fig. 5.2 has been based on the concep-
tion of an ideal system, with modifications from completely flat response based on what is known of speech and speech perception,
interpreted for the special conditions imposed by foreign-language
teaching requirements.

DISTORTION AND NOISE—A TENTATIVE ANALYSIS

Because of the unavoidable length of the discussion required to
document frequency-response limits and permissible intensity variation,

it might be supposed that distortion and noise were somehow of lesser importance. Nothing could be further from the truth. *In fact, minor deviations from the response characteristics just described are much to be preferred to excessive distortion and noise, which can completely nullify the advantages of adequate frequency response.* But some distortion and noise is always present in measureable amounts even in systems of the highest attainable quality, and difficulties arise when one attempts to specify their permissible limits.

Gross underspecification of distortion percentages and signal-to-noise ratios, however, has been inhibited by recent tendencies in commercial electronic design. For example, most current models of amplifiers designed for commercial sound-applications, in which both speech and music are to be reproduced, claim 5 per cent total harmonic distortion,[1] and this percentage is easily achievable at modest cost.

There are no studies which bear directly on our problem, such as, for example, foreign-language learning experiments with controlled amounts of different types of distortion and different signal-to-noise ratios as variables. It has been noted that excessive distortion and noise can produce masking effects[2] and listener fatigue. But one prominent investigator has stated informally that as much as 10 per cent each of harmonic and intermodulation distortion is not demonstrably harmful to the phonetic details which interest us in language teaching. Lacking contrary evidence, let us accept this opinion for the moment. There are two reasons why this percentage seems large: (1) many language laboratory systems *claim* distortion percentages much lower than 10 per cent, but *deliver* much higher ones; (2) anyone who has listened to the average reproduction found in most operating language laboratories (especially to copies of tapes made by the usual student recorder), and compared it directly with the reproduction provided under the same conditions by top-quality professional equipment, cannot fail to receive the impression that the latter quality of reproduction is clearer, quieter, more natural, and more pleasing to the ear. It is no coincidence that such professional equipment, while expensive, does indeed have very low levels of distortion and noise. The specifications we shall develop

---

[1] This figure is used as a reference point for audio amplifier measurements in Publication SE-104 of the Electronic Industries Association: *Audio Amplifiers, Engineering Specifications* (May, 1949).

[2] Cf., for example, the signal-to-noise ratios used in the experimentation reported by Miller and Nicely, 'An analysis of perceptual confusions among English consonants', *Journal of the Acoustical Society of America*, 27 (1955), 338-52.

here will be based on the assumption that such a subjective comparative evaluation derives from the listener's intuitive judgments concerning which system *he would rather listen to for the longest period of time*. The cleaner, quieter system is then the system with the lower potential for causing listener fatigue. This fatigue-potential is of obvious importance in any recording and reproducing system which must provide good learning conditions.

There is experimental evidence to support the view that listeners are sensitive to distortion. Listeners to recorded speech and music (good discs and direct-wire transmission from a radio studio) prefer a narrow or medium frequency range to a wide one.[1] These findings could be explained in either of two ways: (1) years of listening to restricted frequency-range reproduction could lead listeners to suppose that such is the natural, and hence 'preferred' type of reproduction; (2) unpleasant distortion products evident in the wider frequency range are eliminated when the range is restricted. Let us bear in mind that the 'wide range' used in this experiment, performed in 1945, was heard over equipment with distortion characteristics probably inferior to the best high-fidelity equipment available today. If we assume that there were, indeed, noticeable high-frequency distortion components in the 'wide range' used by Chinn and Eisenberg, we find strong support for the second explanation in another experiment. Listeners prefer *unmodified, live* speech or music (i.e. the widest possible range) to speech or music which has been *acoustically* modified in a way which restricts the live sound to a frequency range very much like that of Chinn and Eisenberg's medium range. Such acoustic modification means using special concealed acoustic filters, which do not involve any electronic equipment, and hence no harmonic distortion.[2] The conclusion that noticeable distortion will be rejected by many listeners is further supported by the observation that the suffering families of music en-

---

[1] Chinn and Eisenberg, *Proceedings of the Institute of Radio Engineers*, 33/9 (1945), 571, as reported in H. F. Olson, *Musical Engineering* (New York: McGraw-Hill Book Company, 1952), 349. In this experiment the actual frequency ranges were: narrow = —20 db at 100 cps, 0 db 200-4,000 cps, —30 db at 8,000 cps; medium = —20 db. at 40 cps, 0 db 100-5,000 cps, —20 db at 10,000 cps; wide = 0 db 50-10,000 cps, —30 db at 12,500 cps.

[2] Olson, op. cit., 351-2. The frequency characteristics of the live sound were slightly modified (±2 db to 15,000 cps) by the properties of a cloth curtain used to conceal the filters. With the filters in the restricted-range position, high frequencies were limited to about 5,000 cps.

thusiasts with high-fidelity aspirations and low budgets will finally insist on turning down the treble control in order to minimize the wiry harshness of the loud but distorted top end.[1]

On the basis of these experiments we can now agree that listeners prefer to listen to reproduced speech characterized by low levels of distortion. This subjective preference, let us remember, is here interpreted as an indicator of low fatigue-potential. Another experiment will now give us some clues to determining *how much* distortion is permissible in this application.

Olson[2] reports an investigation of listeners' subjective evaluation of the effect of controlled amounts of distortion in five different frequency ranges. The frequency range most desirable for language laboratories has already been determined in a previous section of this chapter, and corresponds quite closely to Olson's range 4, which was reasonably flat to 8,500 cps, with fairly rapid attenuation above that frequency. Using a basic reproducing system with very low distortion, controlled amounts of harmonic distortion were introduced. For this range, listeners found that about 1 per cent distortion was just perceptible, 3 per cent was considered 'tolerable', and 5 per cent was branded as 'objectionable'.[3] The latter two terms were necessarily loosely defined, tolerable distortion being said to mean the amount of distortion which 'could be allowed in low-grade commercial sound reproduction'. By objectionable distortion was meant the amount of distortion 'which would be definitely unsatisfactory for the reproduction of sound in phonograph and radio systems'. For language laboratories it would then not seem unreasonable to conclude that a distortion percentage falling between perceptible and tolerable would provide a suitably low fatigue-potential. This minimum figure would then be 2 per cent total harmonic distortion, at operating level. Superior equipment would achieve this minimum at *maximum output*, which would then provide negligible harmonic distortion at normal listening levels.

It has already been suggested that harmonic distortion is not the only type of distortion which must be specified. The distortion products

---

[1] True reproduction of the extreme top requires, for music, vanishingly low levels of distortion and noise, available only in more expensive equipment.

[2] Op. cit., 345-8.

[3] While the actual relationships are quite complex, the apparent contradiction between this 'objectionable' percentage and the 5 per cent cited on p. 65 for good commercial amplifiers derives from the fact that the latter is usually measured at rated power output, providing lower distortion at the lower power levels usually used.

which caused listeners to reject wide-range reproduction in the experiment reported by Chinn and Eisenberg no doubt included not only harmonic distortion, but other types as well. Although intermodulation distortion is said to be particularly disturbing, there is no experimentation known to the writer which permits evaluation of the effects of various percentages. The recommended figure is 2 per cent, based on current good engineering practices. An increase in noise level no doubt also contributed to the rejection of wide-range reproduction, but, again, there is no experimentation which permits quantification, and, as in the case of intermodulation distortion, we must rely on current good engineering practices for an estimate of permissible limits. In practice, both distortion and noise are best specified for the pertinent individual components of a language laboratory system, and this will be done as individual components are treated in turn.

Future research in this field must also investigate the fatigue effects of what is called *transient distortion*. Transients are the sudden, sharp, percussion-like sounds frequently heard in music. It is possible to view speech as having a high percentage of such sounds. If these transients are not accurately reproduced, speech may sound blurred and unnatural. But good transient response requires an extremely wide frequency range, with its attendant low harmonic-distortion requirements.[1] If poor transient response should prove to contribute significantly to listener fatigue, our estimates of the frequency-response and distortion requirements of language laboratories would require considerable revision. It is quite possible that it is the better transient response furnished by wide-range, low-distortion equipment which has led some authorities to conclude that frequencies above 10,000 cps contribute to the naturalness of speech reproduction.

SYSTEM VERSUS COMPONENT SPECIFICATIONS

The ideal specifications we have developed above for frequency response, distortion, and noise are those of a complete system, and are intended to characterize sound as heard in the student's headphones. In the sections on frequency response, certain limitations on total-system performance were occasionally implied, but not considered in detail. This was done deliberately, in order not to obscure the discussion. The actual state of affairs is this: by actual measurement, we

---

[1] See G. A. Briggs and H. H. Garner, *Amplifiers* (Bradford, Yorkshire: Wharfedale Wireless Works, 1952), 13-15.

can tell when the performance of a complete system, from programme source to student headphones, is inferior, and we can tell when it is good, but we cannot be sure that it has actually met our ideal specifications. The reason for this peculiar state of affairs is to be found in certain problems presented by the testing of headphones, in the frequency range from 6,000 cps upward, which will be discussed in detail (see pp. 82-7).

There are other limitations on the whole concept of total-system performance. Certainly the quality of the sound the student hears in his headphones is what counts. But it is inviting to suppose that no total system can be any better than its poorest component. A corollary of this approach, however, can lead to the specious view that, since there are at present no headphones which can match the performance of a good amplifier, there is no point in worrying about the specifications of the amplifier.

This point of view is short-sighted, dangerous, and not even true. It is short-sighted because it places the consumer in the position of discovering, for example, at a later date, after he has purchased new headphones which represent a real advance in design and a much closer approximation to ideal specifications than was possible at the time his equipment was originally purchased, that he is now able to hear amplifier noise and other defects he was unable to hear before. It is dangerous because it invites haphazard amplifier design, with little attention to accurate measurement of frequency response, noise and distortion. And it is not true, since it is well known that a properly designed amplifier can *enhance* the reproduction of relatively poor loudspeakers or headphones. For these reasons, actual system specifications in this guidebook will be confined to procedures involving general engineering practices known to lead to superior results, and numerical specifications will be given only for individual components.

GENERAL SYSTEM SPECIFICATIONS

1. Conservative operation

No valve, transistor, condenser or resistor anywhere in the system shall be operated in excess of the maximum ratings specified by the component manufacturer for the class of operation involved. These components are not usually made by language laboratory manufacturers but are supplied by a few companies to the entire industry, and the ratings of such components are available from those manufacturers.

Language laboratory manufacturers or their agents should be required to guarantee that this specific condition is met by their system, since operating components in excess of ratings is not uncommon practice. The consequence is small initial economy, leading to excessive heat generation, short life, and frequent failure.

2. *Extraneous noise*

Extraneous noise, including hum, cross-talk, frying noises, feed-back under normal operating conditions, microphonics, and switching transients, should be inaudible at normal listening level. But the manufacturer or installing firm should not be held responsible for the existence of extraneous noise due to causes beyond his control, such as, for example, interference from nearby radio or television trans-mitters, from unshielded or unsuppressed electronic apparatus in the same building or nearby buildings, or from fluorescent lighting. The manufacturer or installing firm should, however, exercise all due care in seeking to predict and avoid such interference.

3. *Heavy-duty equipment*

(a) *Tape recorders.* It is not possible to specify ruggedness of mechanical equipment in any useful way. Yet, since many of the tape recorders still being used in language laboratory systems were designed originally for the home recording market, the consumer needs some assurance that the particular machine will withstand the exacting operating con-ditions normal in language laboratory use. A number of systems recently made available, or now under development, use new designs more in keeping with these stringent requirements and these units should receive full consideration. Minor circuit and switching modifi-cations of home-type machines to make them work in language laboratory applications constitute no guarantee that the basic mechani-cal features have been redesigned for greater ruggedness, and, hence, greater reliability. The statement 'especially designed for language laboratory service' is quite meaningless in this connexion. The manu-facturer should be required to subscribe to either, but not both, of these statements: (1) the tape recorder units used in this system are (brand name) units, originally designed for home service; (2) the basic mechanical design of the tape recorder units used is not that of units originally designed for home service; the top plate, motor(s), clutch and braking system, and operating controls have been chosen and built to withstand the rigours of institutional use.

(*b*) *Headbands, cords and plugs.* Many breakdowns at student positions are due to defective cords and plugs. Headbands break at various points in the assembly, causing maladjustment of the phones on the student's ears, or making it impossible to put them on at all. There is nothing electronically or mechanically mysterious about this kind of breakdown, but the result is just as disturbing as if a major electronic component had developed a serious defect. The headbands on headphones, therefore, and the cords and plugs furnished with headphones and microphones, should also be designed to withstand the rigours of institutional use. The manufacturer should furnish written evidence that these items have a good service record. If the items proposed are a new development, the manufacturer should furnish a description of the testing procedures used to establish their durability.

(*c*) *Control knobs.* Control knobs on volume controls and switches often persist in coming loose. The result is frequently an inoperative student position. Such control knobs should therefore be either double set-screw types, or equivalent types designed for trouble-free operation. Round-shaft controls with single set-screws should be considered unacceptable.

(*d*) *Volume controls.* Students will sometimes, absent-mindedly or maliciously, try to twist a volume control beyond the stop which is usually found at the point of maximum rotation. The effect is to loosen the control knob and break down the stop. Preference should, therefore, be given to volume controls which incorporate special features designed to increase ruggedness and reliability. Conventional types shall, however, be considered acceptable.

4. Switches

Switches used in monitoring and intercom circuits should be self-cleaning, with either silver- or gold-plated contacts. Rotary programme-selector switches installed at student positions in library systems should be of extremely heavy-duty construction.

5. Tape breakage

It should be impossible to cause breakage or spillage of tape through manual operation of tape-recorder controls.

6. Balanced levels

The system should be so designed that at a satisfactory volume level in any mode of operation (record, playback, listen, intercom, monitor) switching to another mode will not cause disturbing changes in volume. In operating the intercom system, teachers must, of course, become familiar with proper microphone technique. They must learn the best talking distance and speech level which their own voice requires at a given volume setting of the equipment.

7. Constant output with varying load

When student positions are switched to or from a given programme source, students at the remaining positions should experience no disturbing changes in volume. This means that the system output circuitry must be such that the output level does not vary more than 3 db from no load to full load.

8. Impedance matching

In a complex technical field, it is natural for the layman occasionally to seize on some frequently mentioned technical consideration, and overwork it. Such is currently the case with the 'matching' of components. It is often said that if impedances, whatever they may be, are matched, all is well. Unfortunately, as is the case with many other technical terms, no simple meaning attaches to the idea of matching which permits easy generalizations. There is no simple standard by which the layman can judge whether impedances should or should not be matched, or whether low impedance is better than high impedance, or vice versa. These questions are virtually meaningless unless the exact context is known.

The term *impedance*, measured in ohms, quantifies conditions of energy transfer, and these conditions are chosen by the system designer. For this reason, complete systems available under a given brand name give the consumer the best chance of getting high-quality, quiet, trouble-free operation, since the energy-transfer or 'matching' problems have of necessity been worked out for the particular system. If they have not, it will be impossible to meet many of the general specifications above, and pass the subjective tests to be suggested in Chapter 6. It should therefore be specified only that impedance and compatibility considerations be observed in accordance with the basic design of the complete system, and in accordance with approved engineering practices.

A practical problem can arise, however, in the purchase of replacement headphones and microphones, or in adding new features or improvements to existing facilities. Here is a simple rule which should afford the consumer protection against costly mistakes. Consult with the original equipment manufacturer or a fully qualified electronics engineer to determine if a contemplated purchase is compatible with the existing installation. It is quite possible, for example, to purchase better microphones or headphones, and find that the desired improvement cannot be achieved without expensive and frequently compromising modifications to the system itself. This says nothing whatever about the quality of the original equipment. Car tyres of different qualities have their place in the market, and improvements are constantly being made, but the finest tyre made, or the biggest bargain, also has to be the right size for your car.

9. Provision for expansion

Initial wiring should provide sufficient cable for all present and future distribution needs, including eventual installation of tape recorders at all student positions. At least one additional spare line, over and above presently foreseeable requirements, should be included in each distribution cable, to account both for possible short circuits in multiconductor cable, and for future developments. Wiring is relatively inexpensive when furnished as part of the original installation, but very expensive to install later.

10. Easy accessibility

All individual components should be readily accessible for service. Ideally, it should be possible to disconnect any component by unplugging it.

11. Line terminations

Distribution lines should terminate, at both console and student positions, in tag-strips or other suitable junction hardware, to permit efficient trouble-shooting. Line terminations should be identified by labelling of tag-strips or by a chart which identifies colour-coded lines.

12. Component parts lists and schematics

The most rugged and dependable equipment requires a maintenance programme (see Chapter 7) and will eventually require service and replacement of some components. To assure ready access to necessary replacement parts and essential service data, the manufacturer should supply: (*a*) a parts list for each component sub-assembly, which distinguishes between standard parts—those readily available from electronics parts dealers—and parts of proprietary design, available only from the manufacturer; (*b*) an accurate schematic diagram of each component sub-assembly, to facilitate diagnosis of circuit and component malfunction, component replacement, and circuit and mechanical adjustment.

13. System wiring diagrams

In addition to the component parts lists and schematics described above, the manufacturer or installing firm should supply with their proposal a wiring diagram of a typical installation, to suggest proper installation techniques, and to indicate the method and materials for interconnection of the various major units. Upon completion, a detailed wiring diagram of the final installation should be supplied, to indicate wire location, the location of junctions, connections made at junctions, the type of connectors, wire coding, and any other data considered essential for efficient service.

SIMPLICITY AND EFFICIENCY OF OPERATION

The physical arrangement of controls and switches should provide maximum simplicity and operating efficiency for both teacher and student. Adequate 'human engineering' of the many operating controls at the teacher's console is perhaps the most important requirement in language laboratory design, after sound-quality and reliability considerations have been satisfied. Lip-service is always given to these considerations, yet channel selectors and monitor-intercom switches are often presented to the always harassed and sometimes frightened teacher in a bewilderingly complex array. Involved sequencing operations more reminiscent of space-ship control than language teaching are not infrequently required to achieve some simple result. Switch A must be turned to position 2 and switch B to position 6 before button C is depressed and lever D is raised. Such complexity is deeply disturbing to many teachers, and it is small wonder that many of them throw up their hands in despair.

Quite aside from this, time is of the essence in foreign-language teaching. The number of students whose practice can be individually guided by the teacher in a given laboratory period is of major importance in all situations in which the materials used are not designed for self-instruction. Economy in the number and variety of hand motions required, for example, to monitor a single student, evaluate his performance, talk with the student, and move on to the next, can add many profitable minutes to any laboratory session. No time-and-motion studies are available, but manufacturers would perform a great service for teacher and student alike, if they were to conduct such studies and guide their design efforts accordingly.

Simplicity and efficiency cannot, of course, be precisely specified. But, even if time-and-motion studies are not presently available, teachers and purchasing personnel should examine competitive equipment from this point of view, perhaps making some simple time-and-motion observations themselves. Specifications should at least indicate to the prospective supplier that his equipment will be so evaluated (see Appendix A, pp. 111 and 112, items 4.3.13 and 5.4.5). Here are some general guidelines for an evaluation of this kind. For each system under consideration, are monitor-intercom switches arranged to conform to the physical location of student stations? They should be. How many controls must be set to perform a given function? How many controls have to be operated in sequence to achieve a desired result? The fewer the better. Are both hands required? For how many functions? Must the teacher's hands be extended wide one moment, drawn rapidly toward the body the next? Such movements are both tiring and time consuming. Measure, using a stop-watch, the actual time required to complete a monitoring cycle, i.e. to listen and evaluate for thirty seconds, to communicate with the student for thirty seconds, and to listen to the next for thirty seconds. The time over ninety seconds is the time required to perform the various switching operations. Obviously, the less time the better.

The student position is, of course, simpler, but can be subjected to the same kind of analysis. This is especially important if the student has his own tape recorder.

THE QUALITY OF STUDENT VERSUS TEACHER EQUIPMENT

It has been common practice to specify lower performance figures for student equipment than for teacher equipment. The rationale has been that teacher equipment is often used for making master tapes, and often feeds lesson material directly to the student's headphones. It has also been stated that conditions prevailing in student booths do not provide sufficient acoustical isolation for high-quality recordings. These arguments are regarded as untenable. In many language laboratory situations, lesson materials are regularly recorded on to student recorders, so that the student may proceed independently, making maximum use of the listen-record-compare facilities often provided. Our concern must be for the quality of the sound the student hears. For this reason, no distinction is made in this guidebook between performance requirements for teacher and student equipment, with the single exception of the need for at least one very high quality microphone for making master tapes.

COMPONENT SPECIFICATIONS

1. The amplifier

For many reasons, the amplifier should be considered the heart of the language laboratory system. They are used in every installation, as part of tape recorders, or to feed the student headphones directly (normally housed in the teacher's console), or, in audio-active systems, as student amplifiers, normally located at the student position. The number and location of amplifiers are functions of the total design of the system, and cannot be specified precisely, except for a particular installation at a particular institution. Nor is this necessary, since there are no optimum numbers or optimum locations.

The cost of amplifiers which must exhibit optimum frequency range, low limits of intensity variation, as well as low distortion and noise, is a function of the power requirements. Since language laboratory power requirements are usually relatively low, the amplifier is the one component which can be built to exhibit optimum characteristics at very low cost. Amplifiers built to the following specifications should never need replacement on the basis of advances in design. It is strongly recommended that modular construction, using either valves or transistors, be used, and that one basic amplifier be used wherever required in the system, if possible. Modular construction permits simple replacement of the whole amplifier unit in the case of failure, and all emergency electronic service is reduced to a simple plug-in operation. The choice of valves or transistors, if the first system specification of conservative operation is met, is up to the designers. At the current stage of development, no amplifier should be rejected *because* it uses valves, or *because* it uses transistors. In interpreting amplifier specifications, it should be borne in mind that they must have characteristics exceeding the expected performance of the entire system by a considerable margin, so that the unavoidable deficiencies of other components (principally headphones) will be better controlled,[1] and to permit shaping the tonal balance and response curve of the system, as described previously, without introducing additional distortion.

All measurements shall be made at maximum signal level.[2] No adjustment shall be made to secure best readings for each test. The sample specifications given assume a maximum signal of zero line level, 1·89 volts RMS across 600 ohms, or 6 milliwatts. The manufacturer is free to choose amplifier features and design parameters consistent with the total system design, but the performance specifications should agree closely with those given below.

Input sensitivity:	1 millivolt, RMS (−60 db)
Frequency response: (measured by standard gainset techniques)	150-12,000 cps ±1 db 100-15,000 cps ±2 db 60-20,000 cps ±3 db
Total harmonic distortion: (measured by standard wave-analyser techniques[3])	2 per cent
Intermodulation distortion: (using 60 to 6,000 cps, four-to-one ratio)	2 per cent
Signal-to-noise ratio:	60 db below 6 milliwatts

In the case of an amplifier operating at higher power levels, care must be exercised in interpreting the figures given for signal-to-noise ratio. If the maximum signal level available were 6 watts instead of 6 milliwatts, and the signal-to-noise ratio were quoted as 60 db below

---

[1] For example, a peak in the amplifier response curve, if by chance matched by a peak in headphone response at the same frequency, can give disastrous results.

[2] But see footnote 3, below.

[3] In the case of total harmonic distortion, 2 per cent shall be considered to be the maximum permissible at operating level. Superior systems, however, will make this measurement at maximum signal level, or in the case of amplifiers operating at higher power, at maximum power output.

maximum output, the actual ratio would be 60—30, or only 30 db, which is not an impressive figure. Six watts referred to 6 milliwatts is 30 db and must be subtracted from the performance figure given. Conversion figures from watts to db for the common reference levels are given in H. Burrell Haddon, *High Quality Sound Production and Reproduction* (Iliffe Books, 1962), 261.

2. The tape recorder

Frequency response:	7½ ips	100-12,000 cps, ±2 db
		250-6,000 cps ±2 db, no peaks or valleys greater than 1 db (see pp. 58 and 64)
	3¾ ips	100-8,000 cps ±3 db
		250-6,000 cps ±2 db, no peaks or valleys greater than 1 db (see pp. 58 and 64)

Signal-to-Noise Ratio:	7½ ips	
(Peak record level	dual track	50 db
to unweighted	3¾ ips	
noise)	dual track	45 db

Flutter and Wow:	7½ ips	Not to exceed ·2 per cent RMS
	3¾ ips	Not to exceed ·3 per cent RMS

Peak record level is defined as that level at which the overall (input to output) total RMS harmonic distortion is 3 per cent when measured on a 400 cycle tone. Noise is measured when erasing a signal of peak recording level and in absence of a new signal. Thus, bias and erase noise are included as well as playback amplifier noise. All components between 60 and 15,000 cycles are measured.

Tape recorders are normally supplied with two playing speeds, 7½ and 3¾ ips. Commercial lesson materials are usually available at both speeds. The use of the slower tape speeds permits tape economy, since less tape is required for a given amount of lesson material. However, because of the technical problems of proper equalization (adjusting the circuitry to achieve a given frequency response within stated deviation limits) at two playing speeds, machines which record and play both speeds will exhibit much better sound quality at the faster speed. For this reason it is wise, at the present writing, to use $7\frac{1}{2}$ ips as the standard speed. But, if the specifications set forth above are actually met, $3\frac{3}{4}$ ips can provide adequate quality.

Dual-channel recorders, designed to provide separate programme and student tracks for best utilization of the 'compare' feature (see Chapter 1, page 7, and Chapter 4, pages 37 and 38), may be furnished with either one or two record heads. It is important to specify which type is desired. Machines with only one record head are less expensive, but require that programme material be pre-recorded on to the student's tape before the 'compare' feature can be utilized, a time-consuming process. Two record heads cost more, but permit simultaneous re-recording of both programme material and student repetitions.

3. Tape cassettes

Most language laboratories continue to use tape mechanisms which require that the feed reel be placed in proper position and the tape manually threaded past the heads on to the take-up reel. Despite the possibility of mismanagement by both students and teachers, this system continues to prove more reliable than cassette systems.

In Chapter 4 (pages 36-7) remote-controlled systems were described in which the use of tape cassettes is virtually mandatory. If tape cassettes are thus required in a particular application, a choice will have to be made between a continuous-loop type and reel-to-reel type. The former contains an endless loop of tape which normally cannot be rewound, so that a given section of tape can be located only by playing it all the way through again. This is not a disadvantage if the taped lessons, or units of a programmed course, are kept very short, but the cost of the many cassettes required is a factor which must be considered. Reel-to-reel cassettes are equally costly. In general, the latter have proved somewhat more reliable than the continuous-loop variety. Cassette reliability and utility has in the past been somewhat limited by two factors: (1) distortion of the plastic elements, generally because of excessive heat, which suddenly causes the tape to stop moving; (2) the inconvenience of replacing the contents of a cassette with new recorded material, as is often required in experimental programmes. Much research now concentrates on the development of plastic materials for this application which will provide both greater reliability and lower cost.

At present, therefore, it is impossible to formulate exact specifications for cassettes. But remember that a tape cassette failure disables a programme source or a student position just as completely as does the electronic or mechanical failure of any associated component. When considering the adoption of any cassette system, it would be wise to inquire of other institutions, which have used the particular system, just what their experience has been. If the system is a new development, the manufacturer should provide some indication of the testing procedures used to ensure that they provide reasonable reliability and that new material can be placed in a cassette with reasonable convenience.

4. The disc (record) player

Disc players should be of the manual type, as contrasted with record changers, which are not recommended in this service. For maximum programme flexibility the unit should have the three common playing speeds, $33\frac{1}{3}$, 45 and 78 rpm.[1] The turntable must accommodate a 12-in. record. Two types of unit are suitable: (1) the manual unit popular in more expensive high-fidelity installations, which consists of a separate turntable, tone-arm (the 'arm' which rides over the record) and cartridge (the unit which is installed in the tone arm and contains the needle, or stylus), all of which must be assembled locally or by the equipment supplier; (2) the manual unit designed for more modest high-fidelity service, differing in that the tone arm, is permanently attached to the turntable assembly. For this service, the latter type unit is less expensive and entirely adequate.

Cartridges and needles should be chosen with care. Either magnetic[2] or ceramic cartridges may be used. Magnetic cartridges are to be preferred if the associated amplifier can accommodate the much weaker signal. Some are virtually indestructible. Inexpensive crystal cartridges of the type frequently furnished as replacement units in low-cost, one-piece portable record-players are not acceptable.

Diamond needles are recommended, costing perhaps two to three times as much as sapphires, the next best choice, and lasting 30 to 40 times as long. A sapphire needle is good for about 20 hours of playing time before deterioration of quality and possible damage to records can result. There is no such thing as a 'permanent' needle. Sapphires, or even lesser quality metal types, are sometimes ill-advisedly used in

---

[1] rpm = revolutions per minute.

[2] A cover term for various types, including the popular 'variable reluctance' cartridge.

school service for years, to the utter destruction of records and a resulting quality of reproduction quite impossible in language work. If 78 rpm records are ever to be used—they are now quite rare except in private collections—the cartridge must be a 'turn-over' or 'flip-over' type, since a different needle is required. Installation requirements should include a check of the tracking pressure of the tone-arm to assure protection for the records, and minimize needle wear.

A four-pole induction motor, or a hysteresis-synchronous motor is required.

Technical specifications for disc playing equipment, including items not discussed above, may be summarized as follows:

Unit type:	Manual, with either integral or separate tone-arm
Playing speeds:	$33\frac{1}{3}$, 45, 78 rpm
Motor:	4-pole induction, or hysteresis-synchronous type
Turntable:	12 in. diameter, weight 5 lb. or more
Turntable assembly mounting:	Spring mounting, or other suitable means of isolation from external vibration
Flutter and wow:	Not to exceed ·2 per cent RMS
Rumble[1]	50 db below average recording level
Cartridge type:	Magnetic (requires proper preamplification) or ceramic. Turn-over or flip-over assembly, if required
Stylus (needle):	1-mil (or less) diamond for $33\frac{1}{3}$ and 45 rpm discs. 3-mil sapphire for 78 rpm discs, if required
Vertical stylus force (tracking pressure):	A function of both stylus assembly and tone-arm: 4 to 6 gm. or less[2]

---

[1] *Rumble* is low-frequency noise contributed by a turntable motor or its improper mounting. Excessive rumble can cause distortion even in a system in which the low-frequency response has been reduced in accordance with our established curve, by overloading an amplifier stage prior to the point in the system at which the low-frequency response has been reduced.

[2] But note that too *light* a tracking pressure, for a given cartridge, stylus, and tone-arm, can cause the stylus to skip grooves or slide over the record.

Stylus compliance:	2×10^{-2} cm./dyne. Higher compliance preferable
Frequency response:	A function of both cartridge and stylus. 100-8,500 cps ± 2 db is adequate, but available cartridges actually suitable for this application usually claim 20-20,000 cps ± 2 db

HEADPHONES AND MICROPHONES

The frequency response of headphones and microphones is often stated in the manufacturer's literature *without* indication of intensity deviation ($\pm$x db) over the range. So stated, the claim of achieving a given frequency response is meaningless. The realistic frequency-response requirements formulated in this guide-book are hence often associated with very inexpensive headphones and microphones which neither state nor can meet the intensity deviation limits. In practice, therefore, it will be important to specify, by brand name and model number, a headphone or microphone of known quality, or its equivalent. A qualified technical consultant should be able to give sound advice on this point. See Chapter 3, pages 19-21.

5. The headphones

The ideal headphone for language-laboratory use should have a response from 100-8,500 cps, ± 2 db from 250-6,000 cps, with no sharp peaks or broad valleys in this range, and ± 5 db from 6,000-8,500 cps. It was previously stated (page 69) that existing standard methods for testing headphones do not permit us to tell by measurement whether or not a given headphone meets these ideal specifications. This situation now needs to be explained in some detail.

The testing of headphones involves the use of an 'artificial ear', which includes a coupler, designed to duplicate the characteristics of an average human ear channel, and a laboratory-standard condenser microphone. Testing procedures are prescribed by the American Standards Association.[1] There are several important difficulties. The procedures specified are adequate for testing the frequency range from

---

[1] Publication Z24.9, 1949: *Methods for the Coupler Calibration of Earphones,* American Standards Association, 10 East 40th Street, New York 16, New York.

zero to nearly 6,000 cps,[1] but above the latter frequency the ear itself has resonances which are very difficult to duplicate, and the coupler itself contributes resonances which give a false picture of the actual response. The peaks and valleys seen on performance curves between 6,000 and 9,000 cps may be due to the phones or to the coupler. Below about 300 cps, weighting must be used to simulate the tight coupling to the ear required for adequate response at these frequencies. Then, too, there is no evidence that the results obtained by these testing methods correlate at all well with what the ear actually perceives. Many headphones sound a lot better than they apparently should, especially when fed by high-quality programme sources and amplifiers. Indeed, calibrations of headphones obtained by these methods should never be taken too literally, even over the 0-6,000 range, because the coupler is only a standardized approximation to the real ear conditions, which include cushions, an 'elastic flap' (the *pinna*, or external ear), a semi-rigid base of large mass (the head), etc. Other methods of testing are under development, which use a plastic model of the head, fitted with a rubber pinna, but they are experimental, not widely available, and still provide no approach to the associated problems of perception.

Since, therefore, present testing methods provide no satisfactory indication of headphone performance above 6,000 cps, regardless of what performance curves may indicate, we are forced to restrict our evaluation of available headphones to the range below 6,000 cps.

Headphones recommended for language-laboratory use are of two types: sealed-crystal and dynamic.[2] The former utilizes the so-called 'piezo-electric effect', by which, in this case, varying current produces mechanical 'bending' of a Rochelle salt crystal. The crystal is coupled to a thin plate, or diaphragm, which then vibrates, producing sound. A dynamic headphone, generally speaking, operates like a miniature loudspeaker. A light paperlike cone is fastened to a coil, which is placed in the field of a permanent magnet. This 'voice-coil' is attracted or repelled by the permanent magnet, depending on the instantaneous

---

[1] 'The shape of the coupler has been chosen so that the natural frequencies of these (transverse and longitudinal) modes of vibration coincide, and the effects which they produce cancel each other over a wide frequency range. Thereby the coupler is free from resonance effects at frequencies from 0 to nearly 6,000 cps.' L. Beranek, *Acoustic Measurements* (New York, John Wiley & Sons, Inc., 1959), 743.

[2] The order in which these types are mentioned at various points in this discussion should not be construed to imply preference.

polarity of the varying signal which feeds the coil. Air vibrations set up
by the moving voice-coil and cone are heard as sound.

Frequency response of recommended units. Especially for this guidebook,
sample 'quality' sealed-crystal and dynamic headphones were calibrated, using standard coupler techniques.[1] It must be remembered
that low-frequency response (below 300 cps) is partly a function of the
tightness with which the phone fits the ear. In making a calibration,
this condition is simulated by using sufficient weight on top of the
phone to provide the best possible low-frequency response. Both types
showed very good response from 50-250 cps, the dynamics being
virtually flat from 30 cps. The crystals showed more variation in this
region among the samples tested. In the frequency range from 250-
6,000 cps, where our major interest lies, the crystals showed no more
than a ± 3 db variation, and several samples showed ± 2, which meets
our specification for this range. They are free of peaks and valleys, as
we have defined them, and the several samples yielded equivalent results. The general slope of the curve between 1,000-5,000 cps falls
slightly, however, and this is not considered to be a good characteristic
(see page 58). The dynamics were virtually flat to 1,500 cps but showed
$+4$ at 3,500 cps and between $+7$ and $+8$ at 6,000 cps. This does not
meet our specifications. The first of these 'humps' just misses being a
peak, by our definition, but the second is definitely a peak, which is
considered undesirable. The actual data for the dynamic phone showed
$-1\frac{1}{2}$ db at 2,500 cps, $+4$ db at 3,500 cps and -1 db at 5,000 cps.
Because of this 'hump' in a curve which is otherwise flat to 5,000 cps,
it is difficult to comment on the general slope of the curve.

---

[1] The exact procedure used is as follows: A sweep-frequency signal from a Bruel and
Kjaer (B & K) type 3302 beat-frequency oscillator was applied at up to 2 volts RMS
to a single earphone, with impedances matched. The earphone, without cushion, was
centred over a rigid 6 c.c. coupler (American Standards Association type 1), part of
the B & K type 4151 'artificial ear', which also houses a B & K type 4132 condenser
microphone and a B & K type 2613 cathode follower. Approximately 1,000 grams of
weight was rested on top of the phone. The cathode follower fed a B & K type 2603
microphone amplifier, which, in turn, drove the vertical amplifier of a B & K type
2305 graphic level recorder. The horizontal drive of the recorder was coupled to the
sweep-frequency oscillator, so that the graphic function obtained has the coordinates:
amplitude × log frequency. System calibration permits changing the y-coordinate to
decibels (sound pressure level ref. ·0002 dynes/cm²), yielding the data under discussion.

The writer is greatly indebted to Professor Harlan L. Lane, of the University of
Michigan, for running these calibrations, and for extensive discussion of the results.

Ruggedness. Sealed-crystal units are less rugged than dynamics. It must be said, however, that the traditional fragility of crystal headphones has been greatly exaggerated. The encapsulation process used in sealed-crystal units of modern design renders them much less susceptible to damage through accidental dropping, and the like, than was once the case, or is still the case with inferior units. Dynamics are extremely rugged and are quite unlikely to break if accidentally dropped.

Sensitivity to temperature. Crystal units are sensitive to extremes of temperature, and if stored over the summer in a hot classroom or a cupboard, are likely to be ruined. Dynamic units are unaffected by temperature.

Sensitivity to humidity. Neither sealed-crystals nor dynamics are sensitive to humidity.

Cost. Quality sealed-crystal and dynamic headphones are considered to be relatively expensive, and the average cost of good dynamics is higher than the average cost of good crystals. Within the range of characteristics of the kind we have been discussing, cost is largely a function of the quality-control exercised by the manufacturer, by which he ensures precision assembly, adequate testing, and minimum variability in performance from unit to unit as they come off the production line. A manufacturer may well offer a unit at lower cost, but can then guarantee only a lesser frequency response, the achievement of which may require less expensive quality-control measures.

Other units. Ceramic units, which also utilize the piezo-electric effect, completely overcome temperature and humidity problems, but it has been difficult to produce such units and still maintain the performance and sensitivity levels of the better crystal units. Units which will achieve this performance are currently under development. *Magnetic* headphones are not considered suitable for language laboratory use.

Performance summaries. It is useless to set up specifications which cannot be met. We therefore list below tables of the performance which can be expected from the headphones we have been discussing. Selected frequencies from 100 to 6,000 cps are listed. Remember that present testing methods do not permit evaluation of performance at frequencies higher than this. The consumer must make his choice on the basis of these data, the importance of which has been set forth earlier in this chapter, and on the basis of comparative ruggedness, temperature and humidity sensitivity, and cost. In evaluating lower-cost phones, where cost is a factor, one should give preference to units which show the flattest frequency response from 250-5,000 cps, as interpreted, if possible, by a

	QUALITY SEALED-CRYSTAL	QUALITY DYNAMIC
	DB REFERRED TO 1,000 CPS	
100	−2	+1
250	−2	0
500	−1	0
1,000	0	0
1,500	+2½	0
2,000	+½	−1
3,000	0	+2½
3,500	−1	+4, near-peak
4,000	0	+2½
5,000	0	−1
6,000	+2	+7½, peak

At 1,000 cps, the sealed-crystal unit produces an average sound pressure level of 100 db, ref. ·0002 dynes/cm², in a closed 6 cc rigid chamber, with 2 volts developed across 90,000 ohms. Distortion was not measured, but the manufacturer claims ·25 per cent total harmonic distortion at this sound pressure level.

At 1,000 cps, the dynamic unit produces an average sound pressure level of 108-112 db, ref. ·0002 dynes/cm², in a closed 6 cc rigid chamber, with 1 volt developed across 300 ohms. Distortion was not measured, but the manufacturer claims less than ·5 per cent total harmonic distortion below 130 db.

qualified technical consultant (see Chapter 3, pages 19-21). Subjective listening tests are useful (see Chapter 6), but they must be made with programme sources and tapes which are beyond reproach.

Consumer guidance in headphone selection. Since present testing methods do not provide good correlation between data as recorded and sound as perceived, the best information which can be provided for consumer guidance is that which assures maximum comparability among various makes and models. To this end, the language laboratory firm should obtain from the manufacturer and supply to the consumer's technical consultant the following data:

1. The original manufacturer's brand name and model number of the unit. All language-laboratory companies use the headphones of a very few manufacturers. The list price of this unit can then usually be checked in standard electronics parts catalogues.

2. (a) A graph of the expected performance of the phones (see page 82).

(b) The copy of this graph shall be to a scale which permits readings in decibels ref. 1,000 cps to $\frac{1}{2}$ db. Five db shall occupy no less than $\frac{3}{8}$ inch.[1]

(c) The horizontal scale shall readily accommodate readings from 20 to 20,000 cps, the vertical scale at least 60 db.[2]

(d) Sufficient weighting shall be used to give the best low-frequency response of which the tested unit is capable.

(e) No other coupler adjustments shall be made to improve the indicated performance.

(f) The curve shall not be artificially smoothed at any point.

(g) No amplifier compensation shall be used to give a spurious response indication.

3. A statement of the maximum sound pressure level attainable at 1,000 cps at no more than ·5 per cent total harmonic distortion, and the voltage required across the stated impedance of the unit to produce that level.

For comments concerning the use of combination headphone-microphone units, see page 90.

6. The microphone

The problem of meeting adequate frequency-response specifications in microphones is similar to that already encountered in our discussion of headphones. The electro-acoustical details are rather different, however. The testing of microphones is much simpler, since one can measure electrical rather than acoustical output, and it is merely necessary to compare, over the desired frequency range, the output of the micro-

---

[1] These stipulations conform to the recommendations made in Publication SE-105 of the Electronic Industries Association: *Microphones for Sound Equipment*, p. 8. Microphones will require performance statements similar to those of headphones.
[2] See footnote, above.

phone under test with that of a calibrated, laboratory-standard condenser microphone. Microphones with very flat characteristics and low distortion are widely available, and in common use in professional recording studios. But these precision instruments cost, in some cases, hundreds of pounds, and are not feasible in language laboratory applications.

Microphones suitable for making master tapes for language laboratory use are readily available. Since only one is normally required, cost is not ordinarily a factor. The real problem lies in the selection of a suitable student microphone for audio-active or 'compare' applications. Here, many units are required in a typical installation, and, at the present state of development, cost can become virtually prohibitive. A microphone is required with the same characteristics we have stipulated as ideal for headphones: 100-8,500 cps, ±2 db from 250-6,000 cps, with no sharp peaks or broad valleys (as previously defined) in this range, and ±5 db from 6,000-8,500 cps. Total harmonic distortion should be very low, less than ·5 per cent. These deviation and distortion requirements are simply not available today at anything like feasible cost. The specifications we list, therefore, represent realistic compromises in terms of what is presently available. It remains a challenge to industry to continue to improve the characteristics of lower-cost microphones. This is not to say that good results cannot be achieved. Very good results are obtainable, but always at a cost above the minimum offered in a highly competitive market.

If master lesson tapes are to be made with school facilities, the best investment possible is a high-quality dynamic microphone. If recordings are to be made under average home or office conditions, a cardioid type, which does not accept sound from the back of the microphone, is advisable. A non-directional model is entirely satisfactory if an acoustically treated room is available for recording purposes. There are many excellent ones to choose from, and cost is a good indicator of quality in this case. Suitable units list at around £30, and are available with discount for around £25. The equipment supplier should be asked to recommend a representative brand and model in this price range. The consumer should be sure whether the price quoted is list or net, so that the quality level can be established. The unit chosen must have an impedance[1] to match the input to the recorder or

---

[1] Stated in ohms. 'Low' impedance is 50 to 250 ohms. 'High' impedance (High-Z) is not generally stated numerically. See pp. 72-3 on impedance matching.

amplifier with which it is to be used, and be provided with the proper heavy-duty cord and plug. This same unit can be used at the console for general recording, announcement, and monitoring purposes.

TYPICAL TEACHER-RECORDING MICROPHONE SPECIFICATIONS

Type :	Dynamic
Frequency response :	40-15,000 cps listed 100-10,000 cps ± 5 db or less, generally rising characteristic
Distributional characteristics :	Cardioid or non-directional
Impedance :	High or low as required
Output level :	−55 db (or sufficient to drive the amplifier with which it is to be used)[2]

Student microphones. Microphones generally suitable for student use are usually either dynamic or crystal types. Dynamic microphones of good quality are virtually indestructible. Crystal microphones tend to be more fragile, and sensitive to heat extremes. They are readily ruined by exposure to direct sunlight, or by adverse storage conditions. A related type, the ceramic microphone, has lower output, but is relatively insensitive to humidity extremes, and is less temperature sensitive as well. A good-quality magnetic microphone is sometimes used.

Among the lower-cost units usually required, somewhat better unit-to-unit uniformity of frequency response can be expected from dynamics than from crystals, although, as in the case of headphones, this is largely dependent on the manufacturer's quality control, which, in turn, affects the cost. It is strongly recommended that the minimum-quality crystal microphones of the type generally packaged with home tape recorders be eliminated from consideration. As in the case of headphones, the consumer should be supplied with the original equipment manufacturer's brand name and model number of several representative units, together with accurate, unsmoothed graphs of the frequency response of each one. A reasonable choice can be made by selecting the unit with the flattest frequency response between 250 and 6,000 cps. It should be remembered that peaks and valleys in this area are particularly undesirable, but that the total slope of the curve may

---

[2] In stating microphone output level, **higher negative** decibel figures mean *lower* output, but usually imply *better* quality.

rise slightly. Every consideration should be given to the use of microphones with cardioid directional characteristics, in order to reduce the direct and reflected sound which can enter the back of the microphone.

TYPICAL STUDENT MICROPHONE SPECIFICATIONS

Type:	Dynamic, ceramic, crystal, or magnetic
Frequency response:	100-8,000 cps ±5 db (but see 'Headphones and Microphones', p.82)
Distributional characteristics:	Cardioid or unidirectional
Impedance:	High or low as required
Output level:	−55 db (or sufficient to drive the amplifier with which it is to be used)

Microphone and headphone mountings

An arrangement which provides a one-piece assembly for both headphones and microphones has much to recommend it. The microphone is held at a constant distance from the student's lips, producing more uniform student recordings. The hands are left free for writing or manipulating controls. The only limiting requirement is that the unit be sturdy enough to withstand fairly rough handling. It may be difficult, however, to find a dynamic microphone which can meet the ±5 db specification in the small size required. Desk microphone units are quite acceptable. Gooseneck mountings should be avoided. They are subject to breakage at mechanical joints, and are often extremely noisy when moved.

PHYSICAL SPACE REQUIREMENTS

The space needed for each student position is roughly 24 in. × 30 in., not including seating space. There should be enough space between rows so that a student seated at his position does not prevent easy passage behind him. If a projection screen is used, there must be clear visual access to the bottom of the screen from any position in the room. This will affect the height of the rear and side walls of booths, if used. In new construction, consideration should be given to the improvement of viewing by using curved rows, or a stepped arrangement such as is common in auditoriums. Parallel walls are best avoided.

ACOUSTICAL TREATMENT (NOISE CONTROL)

Good acoustics in a language laboratory is a must. The best approach is to employ an acoustical engineer to make recommendations for the acoustical treatment of the room which is to become the language laboratory, or, in the case of new construction, to incorporate the necessary features into the original design. In the case of existing construction, however, there may be many reasons why it is not possible to employ professional help for this purpose. If certain basic principles are understood, it is quite possible for non-specialists to do an entirely adequate job of what we have called *noise control*. It is important to make a careful distinction between sound *absorption* and sound *isolation*.

Sound absorption. Virtually any room has what is called an *ambient noise level*. Ambient noise is the residual or background noise in the room when the activities appropriate to that room are going on. If this noise originates entirely within the room, part of it consists of direct noise from any given source, such as a person talking or moving, or from apparatus in operation. The total direct noise is increased by reflections from walls, ceiling, and floor. The purpose of acoustical treatment is to reduce reflected noise and thereby reduce the total ambient noise. The usual procedure is to apply acoustical tile, or similar absorptive material, to the ceiling. At the present state of development, acoustical tile is much better than so-called acoustical plaster. Its sound-absorbing characteristics increase with thickness, but vary with frequency. Its absorptive qualities are expressed by a quantity called the *sound-absorption coefficient*, expressed as a percentage. A sound-absorption coefficient of 0·75 means that 75 per cent of the sound reaching the tile will be absorbed. Unfortunately, however, a given sound-absorption coefficient is valid only at a particular frequency, and average measures, sometimes called the *noise-reduction coefficient*, can be misleading. If exact analysis of the requirements by an acoustical engineer is not possible, an acoustical tile should be selected whose sound-absorption coefficient is relatively high in the lower part of the middle range of speech frequencies, say 300 to 1,000 cps. High absorption coefficients much lower in frequency than this, although much to be desired, are hard to obtain in an acoustical tile. For convenient reference, the absorption coefficients of different thicknesses of a typical acoustical tile are shown on the next page.[1]

---

[1] Adone C. Pietrasanta, 'Fundamentals of noise control', *Noise Control*, 1/1 (January, 1955).

As reflected sound is reduced by treating one or more walls, in addition to the ceiling, and even by using carpeting on the floor, the effect in the room is gradually to approach the effect of sound out-of-doors in an area where there are no reflecting surfaces. A room with this quality is said to be *dead*. If all listening is to be by means of headphones, the deader the room the better. But if a loudspeaker system is to be used for any purpose, or if the teacher wishes to communicate directly with students without their headphones on, a completely dead room is not desirable, since some reflected sound facilitates communi-

FREQUENCY IN CPS	THICKNESS $\frac{1}{2}$ in.	$\frac{3}{4}$ in.	1 in.
125	·08	·10	·12
250	·17	·22	·31
500	·55	·73	·96
1,000	·73	·88	·90
2,000	·72	·76	·72
4,000	·68	·66	·64

cation at a distance. It is usually sufficient to treat the ceiling and at least one wall. The student is partially isolated from interfering noise by his headphones, especially if the phones are equipped with ear pads which provide a tight seal between phones and ear.

The presence of booths, with their many dividing partitions, also serves to break up reflected sound, and thus reduce ambient noise. Front and side walls within each booth should receive similar acoustical treatment, which helps to control reflected sound in the immediate vicinity of the student. Effective noise control is especially important when audio-active systems are used, since it reduces the total noise fed into the student's live microphone and returned to his ears electronically amplified. Acoustical tile, however, should probably not be used as a dividing partition in booth construction. It catches dust, loses efficiency when painted, and is easily defaced. For practical reasons, perforated metal construction is better.

Sound isolation. Sound isolation may be a factor in two different ways: (1) preventing unwanted noise from outside sources, for example, from a busy city street or a noisy ventilation system, from reaching the room at all; (2) isolating each student position from noise created by his immediate neighbours.

Porous materials, like acoustical tile, are, by definition, not good materials for sound isolation. For maximum sound isolation, the best solution is a thick, solid wall, or even double walls with an air space separating them. But in new construction, the problem is treated best by avoiding it. Language laboratories should not be placed near busy streets or noisy building equipment. Ventilating systems should use some kind of acoustical duct lining or baffling to reduce the amount of noise reaching the room through the system. The noise of heavy machinery can be reduced by mounting it on rubber, or similar material, to prevent vibration reaching the language laboratory through the floor and hence through the building structure itself. Stationary heavy machinery to which access is not regularly required can be boxed in. In such cases, it is usually necessary to line the insides of the insulating box with sound-absorptive material, such as acoustical tile or fibre glass, so that the noise is not actually increased by reflected sound within the box.

Because the top and rear of the language laboratory booth are open, it is not possible to get large amounts of isolation between booths. We have already noted that sound-absorbing materials cannot, of themselves, provide good sound isolation, since they are porous. But a specially-built dividing partition can nevertheless provide a small amount. Granting these limitations, a typical dividing partition would have perforated metal on both sides, plus a fibre-glass 'sandwich' in between, to provide reflected sound absorption in each booth. The core of the sandwich would be of solid material to provide the small amount of isolation attainable. It is assumed, of course, that when seated normally at his position, the student's head is entirely within the booth. Otherwise there could be no such effect at all. Current research may eventually produce core materials capable of providing more isolation than is presently possible.

6 Testing the Language Laboratory

Let us assume that reliable criteria have been used in making the original choice of the equipment. Let us assume further that the manufacturer has delivered components which, to the best of his knowledge, do meet the specifications agreed upon. There is still a vast difference in technical complexity between a sample demonstration or trial arrangement and a complete multiple-position installation. Hence, the need for precise checking of details of performance.

Equipment for making instrumental measurements of language laboratory performance is seldom available to schools. Such measurements are not easy to make and interpret even under the best of conditions. Perhaps the best procedure is to employ a competent technical consultant, as discussed in Chapter 3, who must agree that the specifications of the system have been properly met by the manufacturer before the installation is approved and final payment made. Properly qualified technical consultants, however, are sometimes hard to find. Certain suggestions are therefore included here which may be of use to school personnel.

The first check should seek to ensure proper mechanical operation of all equipment. Check all tape recorders and tape players for proper tape handling. Controls and switches should work easily. In systems using reel-to-reel tape equipment, tape-travel from reel to reel should be smooth and even. When the tape transport is stopped, tape-motion should cease abruptly, with very little coasting, yet with no apparent tendency to break or distort tape. If a tape-cassette system is used, several different cassettes should be inserted and checked for smooth operation.

Mechanical noise in the room coming from the tape recorders should not be disturbing. Clicks from various switches which must be operated during a class period should not be too loud.

All subsequent checks should seek to ensure proper electronic operation of all equipment as evidenced by the quality of the sound. It has been previously pointed out that instrumental measurements of performance are seldom feasible. But, surprising as it may seem, it is readily possible to check the sound quality of language laboratory systems by ear.[1] One must simply learn what to listen for.

The first sound-quality check should be for extraneous noise. As was stated in Chapter 5, which should be carefully reviewed, these are precisely the kinds of noise for which no quantitative measurements are required anyway, since none of them should be there at normal listening level. If in any mode of operation reproduction is characterized by any of these extraneous noises, then something is wrong and should be brought to the attention of the installing firm. Due to the technical complexity of complete systems, it is quite possible for noises of this kind to be heard in the headphones even though a demonstration or trial system exhibited no such defects. When a tape is played over the system, the only residual noise should be a gentle background hiss, scarcely noticeable beneath the signal when the tape is played at normal volume. In making such a test it is, of course, most important that the tape recording used should have been made on a professional machine using a high-quality microphone so that the quality of the recording itself will not be open to question. A general check of frequency response and distortion characteristics can be made as follows: make a tape recording, again using a professional recorder and microphone, if available. The recording should be made by someone other than the person who is to be the judge of the quality of reproduction when the tape is played over the language laboratory system. Record three lists of English words, about twenty words in each list, in a random order not known to the listener: (1) a list which contrasts the initial and final voiceless *th*-sound as in *thin* and *path* with the initial and final *s*-sound, as in *sin* and *pass*; (2) a list which similarly contrasts *f* and

---

[1] A demonstration tape has been prepared to supplement this discussion. Its purpose is to provide a recorded example of common faults in equipment and installations so that: (a) each fault, easily discernible in the demonstration tape, will be recognized as a deviation from acceptable operation; (b) any similar deviation observed in an operating laboratory can be accurately identified and accurately described for the purpose of reporting maintenance and service requirements. The examples offered by this recording are thus intended to serve as a reference or reminder for the person who will periodically check the equipment for sound quality.

The tape is available at $2.95 net and will be sent post paid. Orders are to be sent, with remittance, to Electronic Industries Association, 1721 DeSales Street, N.W., Washington 6, D.C.

s, e.g. *fin* and *knife* with *sin* and *nice*; (3) a list which similarly contrasts voiceless *th* with *f*, e.g. *thin* and *myth* with *fin* and *miff*.[1] Leave a space between words equal to the time necessary to repeat the word silently, plus about one-half second. The words should be read on to the tape as naturally as possible, using a falling intonation on each word, as if it were a complete sentence. Be careful not to over-pronounce or prolong the fricative consonants. This tape is now played over the system using a tape recorder or tape player at the console. Judging is done from a student position. The listener should be able to determine effortlessly which word is being said, as he takes dictation from each of the recorded lists. Listen briefly at each of the student positions to make sure that the quality is identical in each.

If there are recorders at any of the student positions, a further check will be necessary. Record the test tape, played at the console, on to each of the student machines, using the switching facilities provided. Then working at each booth in turn, record your own voice in the spaces, as if you were a student imitating a master tape. Now play back the tape on the student machine and judge the quality as above, or preferably, have still another person judge it. If anywhere *th*, *f*, and *s* are not clearly and independently distinguishable under any of these conditions, then something is wrong. If the background noise (hiss) heard from the student machine while playing back this tape is noticeably louder than that heard when the original tape was played from the console, this fact should be brought to the attention of the installer.

An installation may pass these tests and yet have an unnatural, excessively tinny sound. Make another recording, again on a professional recorder if available. Two voices, a woman's and a man's, should be used, each reading alternate lines of a passage of connected

---

[1] Suitable random lists are given here for convenience: (1) thick, path, moss, bass (rhyme with pass), sigh, song, myth, thong, thaw, mass, bath, math, saw, sick, thin, pass, miss, moth, thigh, sin; (2) seal, Russ, fin, four, sore, sign, knife, miss, gaff, rough, sad, feel, gas, fad, miff, sin, fine, chafe, nice, chase; (3) throw, loath, baff, fad, oath, free, fro, bath, three, Ruth, Thad, miff, thin, roof (Rufe), thigh, fie, loaf, fin, myth, oaf.

Nonsense syllables are more reliable than English words, but introduce writing problems which complicate testing.

These lists do not test frequency response much above 4,000 cps, because, if frequencies above 6,500 cps are absent, the low-frequency component (1,000-2,000 cps) of *f* and *th* will serve as a cue to distinguish them from *s*. The distinction between *f* and *th* is not carried by the friction noise, but by the adjacent vowel. See Chapter 5, pp. 58-61. But tests based on these word lists will reveal excessive distortion and noise which tend to make the fricatives sound alike.

prose. The woman's voice should be an average soprano, the man's a medium baritone. When played over the system, or recorded on to the student recorders, if the woman's voice sounds natural and the man's does not, the system is not adequately reproducing the lower tones which are characteristic of the male voice.

These tests, when recorded on professional equipment as recommended, will test the *playback* capabilities of the console equipment, and the record-playback capabilities of student equipment. To test the recording capability of the console equipment, the test tape should be remade or copied, now using a console recorder, and then replayed for judging.

A comparison should now be made of the relative volume available in the student's headphones as the equipment is placed in various modes of operation. For example, the teacher's voice as it comes over the intercom system should be at the same general level as recorded material.[1] There should be no sudden changes in volume in switching from one mode of operation to another, assuming that all volume controls are set properly.

Check for comparable volume at each student position when a tape is being played over the system. All positions should sound about the same at the same relative setting of the volume control. Differences are sometimes due to defective headphones.

Make sure that there are no clicks in the student's headphones when monitor switches are operated at the teacher's console.

The manufacturer or installing firm must correct any malfunction discovered as a result of these checking procedures. Ordinarily, the installing firm will discover such problems, if they exist, and correct them with little difficulty. But it occasionally happens that the technician responsible is not acutely aware of the need for quiet, clean, distortion-free reproduction of speech, and may consider a certain performance level as adequate, whereas it is in fact not adequate at all. In such case, both school and manufacturer will benefit by having the matters in question brought to the latter's attention as quickly as possible.

[1] But see Chapter 5, page 72, item 6.

7 Servicing and Maintaining the Language Laboratory

EMERGENCY SERVICE

It is important to make a clear distinction between service and maintenance. The term 'service' can mean either routine service or emergency service, but is normally understood to mean the latter. Contractual arrangements must be made either with the installing firm or an approved local electronics firm to provide prompt emergency service. Routine service should be a part of a general maintenance programme designed to ensure high-quality operation of the language laboratory at all times. It will be best for the purposes of this discussion to limit our definition of service to emergency service and to consider all other service procedures as part of the general maintenance programme.

Fig. 7.1. Actually there should be little need for emergency service.

Actually, there should be little need for emergency service. The need for such service develops out of certain practices which are, unfortunately, common in many school situations. For example, it is customary not to worry about the operation of equipment of this kind until it breaks down. It cannot be too strongly stressed that any kind of electronic or mechanical failure during a period in which a regular class is using the language laboratory is a disturbance of the most serious kind. Class schedules and, indeed, the effectiveness of the entire programme can be adversely affected.

PREVENTIVE MAINTENANCE

The key is preventive maintenance. Every effort must be made to ensure that breakdowns do not occur while instruction is in progress. The need for emergency service is only in part a function of the quality of the equipment which has been purchased. A look at the maintenance practices of high-fidelity recording studios will make this point clear. These studios normally use the finest recording equipment that the state of the art has produced. Even so, certain maintenance procedures are regarded as routine and are performed daily, or even oftener, on equipment which, as has been pointed out, is the finest available. Since much language laboratory equipment is not of this quality, the need for preventive maintenance becomes even more urgent. *The essential commodity which the language laboratory must make constantly available is high-quality reproduction of sound.* In view of this, and the time, effort and expense which the selection and installation of the language laboratory entail, it is clearly both poor economy and poor pedagogy not to include rigid preventive-maintenance procedures as a part of any language laboratory programme. Fortunately, the kinds of procedure necessary to ensure trouble-free operation of any good equipment are quite simple, and the techniques can readily be acquired by school maintenance departments and even by student help.

Gradual deterioration of sound quality can be hard to detect because the day to day differences are not obvious, but it is a common experience after several months of operation with no attention to preventive maintenance to get a vague general impression that the sound quality is just not as good as it once was. This vague impression is caused by increases in distortion and noise which can nullify all the care which was used in selecting the equipment in the first place, and add substantially to listening fatigue.

Systematic control of gradual deterioration in sound quality can be achieved as follows. A master tape is made on a professional recorder. This may be the test tape of fricative consonants suggested in Chapter 6. A recording of this tape is then made on all machines used as programme sources and on all student machines. Each test-tape copy is dated and marked with a number identifying the machine on which it was made. At periodic intervals a new copy of the master test tape is made on each machine, and appropriately numbered and dated. A comparison of the original copy made on a given machine with a subsequent copy made on the same machine, both being played on a professional machine in good operating condition, gives a concrete

Fig. 7.2. Gradual deterioration of sound quality can be hard to detect.

indication of any deterioration in sound quality, and provides convincing evidence of service needs in cases which may not be obvious.

The causes of either gradual or sudden deterioration in sound quality may be either mechanical or electronic or both, and can be minimized by the simple maintenance procedures described below.

POTENTIAL MECHANICAL FAILURE
The tape recorder
The chief source of mechanical difficulties is the tape recorder itself. If certain routine maintenance procedures are not followed, the sound quality will deteriorate badly and mechanical operation will become very erratic. The most vulnerable points in a tape-recorder mechanism are these. All rubber or rubber-like surfaces (idler wheels, drive wheels, capstan rollers); vital non-rubber surfaces are the capstan itself, and the recording and play-back heads. The capstan, the capstan roller, and the tape heads can readily accumulate large deposits of oxide from the tapes played on the machines. A sufficient accumulation can seriously impair the sound quality.[1] All these surfaces require daily

---

[1] So-called 'sandwich' tape eliminates this difficulty, but causes some loss of signal strength at the higher frequencies, which results in a poorer signal-to-noise ratio.

cleaning with a suitable cleaning agent (not carbon tetrachloride!).
The recording and playback heads may be somewhat more effectively
cleaned by means of special cleaning agents recommended by the

Fig. 7.3. If routine maintenance procedures are not followed,
mechanical operation will become very erratic.

manufacturer. The heads should also be demagnetized regularly
according to the recommendations of the manufacturer.

Control knobs

If control knobs on switches and volume controls have been properly
chosen and specified in the first place, they should not give trouble. But
knobs with single set-screws invariably come loose. A daily check of all
control knobs for tightness, as well as for accurate indication of position
where necessary, will prevent much loss of student and teacher time.

POTENTIAL ELECTRONIC FAILURE

It was pointed out in Chapter 6 that the presence of extraneous noise
in the headphones, at normal listening levels, is an almost certain indication that some of the specifications are not being met. If a certain
standard of noise-free operation was originally achieved at the time the
laboratory was installed, changes in the kinds of noise which appear in
the headphones at any student position can be important clues to
potential electronic failure. At least once a week the audio quality
available at each student position should be carefully checked by
critical listening. This listening check can simply repeat the procedures
described in Chapter 6.

Check for the appearance of extraneous noise with no tape playing
anywhere in the system. Then play a tape, first from the console and
then on the student machine. The recorded tape used should be one of
known high quality and low hiss level, and could again be the master
test tape of fricative consonants previously suggested. The appearance

of noise at any student position is a sure sign of potential electronic failure. The most likely source of the trouble is valves. But it may be difficult for school personnel to locate the precise source of the trouble. This is an excellent argument for having sufficient spare amplifiers available so that school personnel need only replace the complete amplifier. The faulty amplifier can then be returned at leisure to the service organization for careful checking.

Fig. 7.4. Extraneous noise in the headphones is an indication that specifications are not being met.

The appearance of any new distortion, fuzziness, or a marked reduction in volume at any student position or at the console is another obvious clue to potential electronic failure. But distortion and volume reduction can also be due to an accumulation of tape deposits on the record or playback heads. This should not occur if the cleaning procedures previously recommended have been followed.

Rotate all volume controls while listening to associated equipment and check for scratching noises. If a faulty volume control is located, it can frequently be remedied by running a drop or two of a suitable quieting agent, readily available in any electronics store, down the shaft of the offending control. If the trouble persists, it should be brought to the attention of the service organization and replaced.

Headphone and microphone cords are frequent offenders. A weekly check of all cords is important. With the equipment turned on and the volume raised to the point where there is residual background noise in the headphones, gently twist the cord at the points where it enters the plug and the headphones. If the sound cuts off or is markedly reduced in volume, or if any scratching noise is heard as the cord is twisted, either the cord or the entire headphone unit should be replaced immediately, as it is sure to give trouble. Microphones may be similarly tested in an audio-active system. If the system is not audio-active, it will be necessary to make a brief recording while twisting the cord, or to speak over the intercom system with another person listening.

All tape recorders in the system should be periodically checked for their continued ability to produce a good, clear recording. Student recorders should be checked at the student position, using the regular student microphone. A defective microphone is a frequent cause of poor recording quality.

In order to avoid uncertainty and confusion, it is important that adequate maintenance records be kept. A detailed schedule of preventive maintenance should be worked out with the advice of the manufacturer or the service agency which supplies emergency service. This schedule should show what is to be checked, how often, by whom, and what the procedure is. The teacher's console and each student position should have a service record card conveniently posted, giving the complete maintenance record of each item of equipment at that position.

Many language laboratory companies are spending much time and effort to provide schools with good equipment at nominal cost, often under severely competitive conditions. To insist on the need for preventive maintenance in no way detracts from the intent and validity of these efforts, but is strictly in accord with the usual practice in all similar situations in which high-quality sound reproduction must be the normal order of the day.

Appendix A. A Sample Specification

The system chosen for sample specification corresponds closely to System V, Chapter 4, pages 34-6. See also Systems III and IV, Chapter 4, pages 29-33. A minimum number of student recorders is specified. This system is fairly typical, but must be construed merely as an example. Changes in general layout, functions and features (but not performance specifications) must be made wherever necessary to conform to the requirements of the particular system desired.

Specifications for acoustical treatment (except booths), air-conditioning, lighting, and the like, are not included, since they depend so completely on the individual situation. Suggestions for the former are included in the discussion of physical space and acoustical considerations in the final section of Chapter 5.

Conditions or features considered optional within this system are marked #.

I. GENERAL CONDITIONS

1.1 This specification describes a selection of interconnected items of electronic and electro-mechanical equipment to be used in connexion with the teaching of foreign languages at (institution), hereinafter termed the *institution*.

1.2 The equipment herein described and specified is to be installed in (room, building, institution, address), and the area so designated, together with the equipment to be installed therein, shall hereinafter be termed the *language laboratory*.

1.3 The institution will eventually negotiate only with a single selling agency, to whom funds will be paid, and who will be responsible for the successful completion of the language laboratory installation. This selling agency, whether the manufacturer, his representative, agent, or duly approved firm of installers, shall hereinafter be termed the *seller*.

1.4 (and such further numbered items as are necessary, should state the requirements dictated by institutional procurement procedures, and by applicable laws and ordinances, especially those relating to the securing of permits and licences, the carrying of insurance, prevailing wage rates, the furnishing of bonds, compliance with construction and electrical codes, etc. The seller should be specifically required to certify that electrical shock hazard is negligible at all points at which the user comes in contact with the equipment, and that, under normal operating conditions, no danger exists of coming into accidental contact with portions of the equipment, such as motors, fans, etc., which would cause injury to students or teachers.)

1.5   (to be renumbered as required by the content of 1.4) Actual installation shall be made by an authorized agent of the manufacturer, who is thoroughly familiar with the equipment, and who shall have available to him, whenever required, the services of a factory engineer.

1.6   The seller shall supply and install all equipment, wire, and incidental hardware necessary for the successful completion of the installation, *except* (detail items to be supplied by the institution, usually only electrical power service and outlets as shown on a specific electrical wiring diagram).

1.7   The seller shall agree to install all equipment in a professional and workmanlike manner, in accordance with good construction and engineering practices.

1.8   The seller shall agree that all performance specifications herein set forth will be regarded as the minimum standard acceptable.

1.9   The seller shall agree to sponsor, as soon as the language laboratory is ready for regular student use, a programme of instruction by a qualified language laboratory specialist to all teachers and other personnel involved in the operation and administration of the laboratory. This programme shall include the necessary minimum of group instruction, plus a single check-out of each individual in the operation of all equipment. See also 3.5.

1.10 The institution reserves the right to withhold final payment for equipment furnished and services rendered by the seller until thirty (30) calendar days shall have elapsed, during which operation shall have included full and satisfactory implementation of all specified functions of all equipment, and performance at least according to the minimum standards set forth in these specifications (# as certified by the institution's designated technical consultant). The last day of this thirty-day period shall be considered the official completion date.

1.11 The seller shall agree to furnish all emergency service, including parts replacement and installation labour, both until the official completion date as determined in 1.10 above, and for a period of one calendar year thereafter. Such service shall be furnished within 24 hours after an authorized service request. Before the official completion date, such service, parts replacement, and installation labour shall be furnished without cost to the institution, except in cases of obvious vandalism. For one calendar year thereafter, such service, parts replacement, and installation labour shall continue to be furnished without cost to the institution except: (a) in cases of obvious vandalism, and (b) in cases of trivial service requests due to failure of teaching personnel to understand the operation of equipment.

1.12 The seller shall furnish an estimate of maintenance costs of the proposed language laboratory, projected for each of two years following the first full year of operation, reckoned from the date of completion as determined in 1.10 above, and a statement of the seller's estimated charges for continuing to supply emergency service. Nothing in this section shall be construed as an obligation upon the institution to continue to use the services of the seller beyond the period specified in 1.11 above.

1.13 The seller shall assist the institution in setting up a suitable preventive-maintenance programme.

2. GENERAL DESCRIPTION

2.1 The language laboratory shall contain a teacher's console with tape and disc programme sources and switching facilities. Monitoring and teacher-student intercommunication facilities shall be provided. There shall be 30 student positions, of which 22 shall each be equipped with headphones and microphone for audio-active listening and responding, and of which 8 shall each be equipped, in addition, with a dual-channel tape recorder.

2.1.1 The term 'audio-active' shall be defined to mean that the student, whether or not he has his own recording facilities, shall be able to listen to any designated programme source, and, while responding or recording, hear his own voice amplified through his own headphone and microphone system.

2.1.2 The term 'dual-channel tape recorder' shall be defined to mean a tape recorder or tape deck which provides separate programme and student tracks, using two[1] record heads and two playback heads. Erasure of the lesson (programme) track shall not be possible at the student position.

3. GENERAL SYSTEM SPECIFICATIONS

3.1 *Conservative operation.* No valve, transistor, condenser, or resistor anywhere in the system shall be operated in excess of the maximum ratings specified by the original parts manufacturer for the class of operation involved.

3.2 *Extraneous noise.* Extraneous noise, including hum, crosstalk, frying noises, feedback under normal operating conditions, microphonics, and

---

[1] Or one record head. See Chapter 5, p. 79.

switching transients, shall be inaudible at normal listening level. But the seller shall not be held responsible for the existence of extraneous noise due to causes beyond his control, such as, for example, interference from nearby radio or television transmitters, from unshielded or unsuppressed electronic apparatus in the same or nearby buildings, or from fluorescent lighting. The seller shall, however, exercise all due care in seeking to predict and avoid such interference.

3.3   *Heavy-duty Equipment*

3.3.1 *Tape recorders.* The seller shall subscribe, in writing, to either, but not both, of the following statements: (*a*) the tape recorder units used are (brand name) units, originally designed for home service; (*b*) the basic mechanical design of the tape-recorder units used is not that of units originally designed for home service. The top plate, motor(s), clutch and braking system, and operating controls have been chosen and built to withstand the rigours of institutional use.

3.3.2 *Headbands, cords and plugs.* The headbands on headphones, and cords and plugs furnished with headphones and microphones, shall likewise have been designed to withstand the rigours of institutional use. The seller shall furnish written evidence that these items have a good service record. If the items proposed are a new development, the seller shall furnish a description of the testing procedures used by the manufacturer to establish their durability.

3.3.3 *Control knobs.* Control knobs on volume controls and switches shall be either double set-screw types, or equivalent types designed for trouble-free operation. Round-shaft controls with single set-screw knobs shall be unacceptable.

3.3.4 *Volume controls,* Preference shall be given to volume controls which incorporate special features designed to increase ruggedness and reliability. Conventional types shall, however, be considered acceptable.

3.4   *Tape breakage.* It shall be impossible to cause breakage or spillage of tape through manual operation of tape recorder controls.

3.5   *Balanced levels.* The system shall be so designed that, at a satisfactory volume in any mode of operation (record, playback, listen, intercom, monitor), switching to another mode will not cause disturbing changes in volume. To assure proper operation of intercom facilities, the seller shall, as part of the instructional programme specified in 1.9, instruct teachers in proper microphone technique, including the best talking distance for a given voice and volume setting.

3.6 *Constant output with varying load.* The system output circuitry shall be such that the output level does not vary more than 3 db from no load to full load.

3.7 *Impedance matching.* Impedance and compatibility considerations shall be observed in accordance with the basic design of the complete system, and in accordance with approved engineering practices.

3.8 *Provision for expansion.* Initial wiring shall provide sufficient cable for all present and future distribution needs, including eventual installation of tape recorders at all student positions. In addition, at least one spare line shall be included in each distribution cable.

3.9 *Easy accessibility.* All individual components shall be readily accessible for service. Wherever feasible, plug-in components shall be used.

3.10 *Line terminations.* Distribution lines shall terminate, at both console and student positions, in tag-strips or other suitable junction hardware, to permit efficient trouble-shooting. Line terminations shall be identified by labelling of tag-strips, or by a chart which identifies colour-coded lines.

3.11 *Component parts lists and schematics.* To assure ready access to necessary replacement parts and essential service data, the seller shall supply: (*a*) a parts list for each component sub-assembly, which distinguishes between standard parts—those readily available from electronics parts dealers—and parts of proprietary design, available only from the manufacturer; (*b*) an accurate schematic diagram of each component sub-assembly to facilitate diagnosis of circuit and component malfunction, component replacement, and circuit and mechanical adjustment.

3.12 *System wiring diagrams.* The seller shall supply with his proposal a wiring diagram of a typical installation, to suggest proper installation techniques, and to indicate the method and materials for interconnexion of the various major units. Upon completion, a detailed wiring diagram of the final installation shall be supplied, to indicate wire location, the location of junctions, connexions made at junctions, the type of connectors, wire coding, and any other data considered essential for efficient service.

4. THE CONSOLE[1]

4.1 *Physical description.* The teacher's console shall be of metal construction, except for the top, which may be of wood, metal, or plastic laminate. The top shall provide a clear writing surface, and shall be at standard desk height. Console equipment shall be so arranged that the teacher

---

[1] Performance specifications for all individual components are grouped in section 8, pp. 113-16.

has a clear view of the room when seated. Space shall be provided in or on the console for up to (number) programme sources, which shall preferably be accessible to the teacher for loading and unloading from the normal seated position.

4.2   *Equipment and accessories.* The console shall be furnished with the following equipment installed:

> 2 two-speed, manual-threading,[1] single-channel, half-track tape recorders, $7\frac{1}{2}$ and $3\frac{1}{3}$ ips.
>
> 1 three-speed manual disc (record) player, $33\frac{1}{3}$, 45, and 78 rpm.
>
> 1 control panel.

The following accessories shall be furnished:

> 1 recording microphone.
> 2 headphones.

4.3   *Equipment functions and associated controls*

4.3.1   A master switch shall control the AC supply to all console equipment.

4.3.2   The tape recorders shall be equipped with controls to implement the following functions: (*a*) AC on-off; (*b*) record-duplicate, recording from any other programme source, from the console microphone, or from the intercom system; (*c*) playback; (*d*) rewind; (*e*) fast forward; (*f*) pause; (*g*) stop. The pause lever or switch shall instantaneously stop the forward motion of the tape in the record-duplicate and playback modes, without turning off the electronics. A volume control shall regulate the record-duplicate volume. A resettable digital counter shall be provided on the tape mechanisms to indicate tape position.

4.3.3   A volume control and VU meter shall be supplied for each programme source (channel), *or* a single VU meter shall be provided on the main control panel, with a selector switch to permit the operator to select the channel to be observed, and the necessary volume controls to permit proper adjustment of each channel.

4.3.4   A positive-indication selector switch shall be used for the selection of programme sources.

4.3.5   Monitoring and intercom switches shall be arranged in rows, geographically orientated to the physical lay-out of student positions in the laboratory.

4.3.6   Switching modes shall be provided to permit monitoring and

[1] See Chapter 5, pp. 79-80 on tape cassettes.

intercommunication with (*a*) any individual student; (*b*) any row of students; (*c*) any combination of individuals and rows; (*d*) the entire class at one time (all-call).[1]

4.3.7 Monitoring of individual students must be silent and undetectable by the monitored student, who must not hear any clicks, pops, or change of volume.

4.3.8 Switches used to implement 4.3.6 shall be self-cleaning, with silver or gold-plated contacts.

#4.3.9 Switching shall be provided to establish 'party-line' connexions between students selected by the teacher.

#4.3.10 Switching shall be provided to permit temporary transfer of a student or group of students to any pre-selected programme, without disturbing students not thus selected.

4.3.11 An extra headphone jack shall be provided for a guest listener.

#4.3.12 A single switch, on the microphone or on the control panel, shall permit simultaneous starting and stopping of all student tape recorders.[2]

4.3.13 The physical arrangement of controls and switches shall provide the maximum simplicity and operating efficiency consistent with the number of specified functions and the meeting of performance requirements. These factors will receive due consideration in evaluating proposals (see Chapter 5, pages 74-5).

5. STUDENT POSITIONS

5.1 *Physical description*[3]

Student positions shall consist of rows of metal booths 30 in. wide, 24 in. deep, with a plastic laminate work surface 29 to 30 in. high. There shall be sufficient space between rows so that a student seated in normal working position does not prevent easy passage behind him. Acoustic barriers shall be provided between booths, 18 in. above the work surface, consisting of rigid, perforated metal on both sides. The core of the acoustic barrier shall be of suitable solid material. A layer of acoustic fibreglass shall cover each side of the core. The legs of the booths shall be adjustable for levelling purposes, and each row shall be anchored to the floor in such a manner as to prevent shifting. The front of the booths shall be fitted with clear $\frac{1}{4}$-in. safety glass for the full height between the work surface and the barriers. There shall be no sharp

---

[1] See Chapter 4, p. 36.

[2] If this option is specified, student tape recorders must be solenoid operated. See Chapter 4, p. 32.

[3] Dimensions are typical.

edges, burrs, or protruding screws on any part of the booths with which a person could come into contact in normal usage.

5.1A (alternate) Student positions shall be installed without dividing partitions at rows of tables, each of which shall be fitted with a plastic laminate top. Each table shall be of normal desk height, with positions installed at 30-inch intervals. Each one shall be anchored to the floor to prevent shifting.

5.2 All wiring shall be in concealed ducts within the structure, and all ducts shall be closed.

5.3 *Equipment*

Student positions, to the extent specified in section 2, shall be provided with the following equipment and accessories installed:

 1 two-speed, dual-channel, manual-threading tape recorder, $7\frac{1}{2}$ and $3\frac{3}{4}$ ips.[1]
 1 student amplifier.[2]
 1 volume control.
 1 set of headphones, with heavy-duty headband, cord and plug.
 1 microphone, with heavy-duty cord and plug.[3]

5.4 *Equipment functions and associated controls*

5.4.1 The student positions shall be audio-active. See section 2 for definition.

5.4.2 Tape recorders, in positions so equipped, shall provide switching modes to implement the following functions: (*a*) AC on-off; (*b*) record-duplicate, recording from microphone or programme source; (*c*) playback; (*d*) rewind; (*e*) fast forward; (#*f*) pause; (*g*) stop. The pause lever or switch shall instantaneously stop forward motion of the tape in the record-duplicate and playback positions, without turning off the electronics. A resettable digital counter shall be provided on the tape mechanism to indicate tape position.

#5.4.3 A meter shall indicate recording or duplicating level.

5.4.4 The volume control shall adjust the volume of the programme source or student recording as heard in the student's headphones.

5.4.5 The physical arrangement of controls and switches shall provide the maximum simplicity and operating efficiency consistent with

[1] For remote-controlled systems, see Chapter 4, pp. 36-7. For tape cassettes, see Chapter 5, pp. 79-80. A single-speed machine may be specified if desired. This requires a prior decision concerning the desired speed. See Chapter 5, p. 78.

[2] If required. An audio-active system may use acoustic amplification.

[3] For microphone and headphones, specify type of mounting. See Chapter 5, p. 90.

the number of specified functions and the meeting of performance requirements. These factors will receive due consideration in evaluating proposals (see Chapter 5, pages 74-5).

6. SPARE COMPONENTS AND ACCESSORIES

1 console tape recorder
1 student tape recorder
3 student amplifiers
3 headphones
3 microphones
12 headphone cords, with plugs attached
12 microphone cords, with plugs attached

7. OTHER EQUIPMENT ACCESSORIES AND SUPPLIES

(Here may be listed professional recording and playback equipment, if desired for making master lesson and test tapes, as well as such items as a bulk eraser, a head demagnetizer, tape, tape splicing equipment, etc.)

8. COMPONENT PERFORMANCE SPECIFICATIONS

8.1   *The Amplifier*[1]

Input sensitivity:	1 millivolt RMS ($-$60 db)
Frequency response:	150-12,000 cps $\pm$1 db
	100-15,000 cps $\pm$2 db
	60-20,000 cps $\pm$3 db
Total harmonic distortion:	preferred, 2 per cent at maximum output; acceptable, 2 per cent at operating level
Intermodulation distortion:	2 per cent, 60 and 6,000 cps, 4 to 1 ratio
Signal-to-noise ratio:	60 db below 6 milliwatts, without reference to maximum output

Standard gainset and wave analyser techniques shall be the basis for frequency response and harmonic distortion measurements respectively.

8.2   *The tape recorder*[2]

Frequency response:	7½ ips	100-12,000 cps $\pm$2 db
		250-6,000 cps $\pm$2 db, no peaks or valleys greater than 1 db
	3¾ ips	100-8,000 cps $\pm$3 db
		250-6,000 cps $\pm$2 db, no peaks or valleys greater than 1 db

---

[1] See Chapter 5, pp. 76-8.

[2] See Chapter 5, pp. 78-9.

Signal-to-noise ratio:	$7\frac{1}{2}$ ips	50 db
(Peak record level to		
unweighted noise)	$3\frac{3}{4}$ ips	45 db
Flutter and Wow:	$7\frac{1}{2}$ ips	not to exceed ·2 per cent RMS
	$3\frac{3}{4}$ ips	not to exceed ·3 per cent RMS

A peak shall be defined as an area of extra amplification less than a quarter-octave wide. A valley shall be defined as an area of attenuation more than a quarter-octave wide. Peak record level is defined as that level at which the overall (input to output) total RMS harmonic distortion is 3 per cent when measured on a 400 cycle tone. Noise is measured when erasing a signal of peak record level, and in absence of a new signal. Thus, bias and erase noise are included, as well as playback amplifier noise. All components between 60 and 15,000 cps are measured.

8.3   *The disc (record) player*[1]

Unit type:	Manual, with either integral or separate tone arm
Playing speeds:	$33\frac{1}{3}$, 45, 78 rpm.
Motor:	4-pole induction, or hysteresis-synchronous type
Turntable:	12 in. diameter; weight, 5 lb. or more
Turntable assembly mounting:	Spring mounting, or other suitable means of isolation from external vibration
Flutter and Wow:	·2 per cent RMS
Rumble:	50 db below average recording level
Cartridge type:	preferred, magnetic (requires proper preamplification); acceptable, ceramic
Stylus (needle):	1-mil (or less) diamond for $33\frac{1}{3}$ and 45 rpm discs; 3-mil sapphire for 78 rpm discs
Vertical stylus force: (*tracking pressure*)	4 to 6 grams, or less. See second footnote, Chapter 5, page 81.
Stylus compliance:	$2+10^{-6}$ cm/dyne. Higher compliance preferable
Frequency response:	100-8,500 cps ± 2 db[2]

Cartridges of the type usually furnished as replacement units in low-cost, one-piece portable record-players shall not be acceptable. The

---

[1] See Chapter 5, pp. 80-2.

[2] In writing this specification, note carefully the statement on cartridge frequency response, Chapter 5, p. 82.

frequency-response characteristics of the cartridge and stylus combination shall be those of (brand name, model number), or equal.

8.4   *The headphone[1]*
The following performance figures shall be considered representative of headphones presently acceptable in this application.

	QUALITY SEALED-CRYSTAL	QUALITY DYNAMIC
	DB REFERRED TO 1,000 CPS	
100	−2	+1
250	−2	0
500	−1	0
1,000	0	0
1,500	+3	0
2,000	+1	−1
3,000	0	+3
3,500	−1	+4
4,000	0	+3
5,000	0	−1
6,000	+2	+8

At 1,000 cps, the sealed-crystal unit shall produce an average sound pressure level of 100 db, ref. ·0002 dynes/cm², in a closed 6 cc rigid chamber, with 2 volts developed across 90,000 ohms. Total harmonic distortion at this sound pressure level shall be less than ·5 per cent.

At 1,000 cps, the dynamic unit shall produce an average sound pressure level of 108-112 db, ref. ·0002 dynes/cm², in a closed 6 cc rigid chamber, with 1 volt developed across 300 ohms. Total harmonic distortion at this sound pressure level shall be less than ·5 per cent.

8.4.1 The seller shall supply to the institution, or to the latter's designated technical consultant, the following data pertaining to all proposed headphones:
    a. The original manufacturer's brand name and model number.
    b. A graph of expected performance.
       1. This graph shall be to a scale which permits reading in decibels ref. 1,000 cps to $\frac{1}{2}$ db. Five db shall occupy no less than $\frac{3}{8}$ inch.
       2. The horizontal scale shall readily accommodate readings from 20-20,000 cps, the vertical scale at least 60 db.

---

[1] See Chapter 5, pp. 82-7, especially the introductory statement on page 82.

c. A statement of the maximum sound pressure level attainable at 1,000 cps at no more than .5 per cent total harmonic distortion, and the voltage required across the stated impedance of the unit to produce that level.

8.4.2 The seller shall certify that the following conditions obtained in making the graphed measurements:

a. Sufficient weighting shall have been used to give the best low-frequency response of which the unit is capable.

b. No other coupler adjustments shall have been made to improve the indicated performance.

c. The curve shall not have been artificially smoothed at any point.

d. No amplifier compensation shall have been used to give a spurious response indication.

8.5   *The microphone*[1]

The seller shall supply to the institution, or to the latter's designated technical consultant, performance graphs of all proposed microphones, which shall conform to headphone graph specifications 8.4.1 a, b 1 and 2, and 8.4.2 c and d.

8.5.1 *Teacher-recording (console) microphone*

Type:	dynamic.
Frequency response:	40-15,000 cps listed, 100-10,000 cps ± 5 db, generally rising characteristic.
Distributional characteristics:	cardioid or non-directional.

Impedance and output level shall be chosen to match the amplifier with which it is to be used. Performance shall be that of (brand name, model number), or equal.

8.5.2 *Student microphone*

Type:	Dynamic, ceramic, crystal or magnetic.
Frequency response:	100-8,000 cps ± 5 db (but see Chapter 5, introductory statement on page 82).
Distributional characteristics:	cardioid or unidirectional.

Impedance and output level shall be chosen to match the amplifier with which it is to be used. Microphones of the type usually packaged with home-type tape recorders shall not be acceptable. Performance shall be that of (brand name, model number), or equal.

---

[1] See Chapter 5, pp. 87-90.

Appendix B. A Select Bibliography of Audio-Visual
Teaching Material

Appendix B. A Select Bibliography of Audio-Visual Teaching Material

KEY TO ABBREVIATED TITLES

Ad. Ed.	*Adult Education* (London).
Am. Sch. & Univ.	*American School and University* (New York).
Arch. J.	*Architect's Journal* (London).
A.P.L. Newsletter	*Association for Programmed Learning Newsletter* (now *Programmed Learning News*) (London).
A.V.I.	*Audiovisual Instruction* (Washington, D.C.).
AVLJ	*Audio-Visual Language Journal* (London).
Babel	*Babel* (New Series). Journal of the Australian Federation of Modern Language Teachers' Associations (Carlton, Victoria).
Can. M.L.R.	*Canadian Modern Language Review* (Toronto).
Design	*Design* (London).
Educ.	*Education* (London).
Ed. D.	*Education Digest* (Ann Arbor, Mich.).
Ed. Screen	*Educational Screen and Audio-visual Guide* (Chicago, Ill.).
Ed. Teach.	*Education for Teaching* (London).
El. Sup.	*Electrical Supervisor* (London).
E.T.L. Newsletter	*Electronic Teaching Laboratories Newsletter* (ceased) (Hagerstown, Maryland).
E.L.T.	*English Language Teaching* (London).
Ét. Ling. App.	*Études de Linguistique Appliquée* (Besançon).
Fr. Monde	*Le Français dans le Monde* (Paris).
Fremdspr.	*Fremdsprachenunterricht* (Berlin, D.D.R.).
Fr. Rev.	*French Review* (Davidson, North Carolina).
Gmn. Qtly.	*German Quarterly* (Syracuse, N.Y.).
Hisp.	*Hispania* (Ada, Oklahoma).
Inc. Ling.	*Incorporated Linguist* (London).
Inostran. Yazyki	*Inostrannye Yazyki v Shkole* (Moscow).
I. J. Ad. Yth. Ed.	*International Journal of Adult & Youth Education* (Unesco).
I.J.A.L.	*International Journal of American Linguistics* (Bloomington, Indiana).
I.R.A.L.	*International Review of Applied Linguistics in Language Teaching* (Heidelberg).

J. Sec. Ed.	*Journal of Secondary Education* (Burlingame, Calif.).
J.S.M.P.T.E.	*Journal of the Society of Motion Picture and Television Engineers* (Easton, Penna.).
L.L.	*Language Learning* (Ann Arbor, Mich.).
Lang. Mod.	*Langues Modernes* (Paris).
Ling. Rep.	*The Linguistic Reporter* (Washington, D.C.).
Listener	*The Listener* (London).
Manager	*The Manager* (London).
M.L.J.	*Modern Language Journal* (St. Louis, Mo.).
Mod. Lang.	*Modern Languages* (London).
N.C.A.V.A.E.	National Committee for Audio-Visual Aids in Education.
N.D.E.A. *F.L. News*	*National Defence Education Act Foreign Language News* (Washington, D.C.)
New Ed.	*New Education* (London).
Off. Arch.	*Official Architecture and Planning* (London).
Pädagogik	*Pädagogik* (Berlin, D.D.R.).
Praxis	*Praxis des neusprachlichen Unterrichts* (Dortmund).
Progress	*Progress* (Unilever Quarterly) (London).
Rev. Ed. Res.	*Review of Educational Research* (Washington, D.C.).
Rev. Phon. App.	*Revue de Phonétique Appliquée* (Mons, Belgium).
Sec. Teach.	*The Secondary Teacher* (Victoria Secondary Teachers' Association).
Taalond.	*Taalonderwijs.*
Tech. Ed.	*Technical Education & Industrial Training* (London).
Tech. J.	*Technical Journal* (Association of Teachers in Technical Institutions) (London).
T.E.S.	*Times Educational Supplement* (London).
Vida Hisp.	*Vida Hispánica* (London).
Vis. Ed.	*Visual Education* (London).
Wis. J. Ed.	*Wisconsin Journal of Education* (Madison, Wis.).

ADAM, J. B. 'Harnessing the language laboratories' *Educ.* vol. 123, 24 Jan. 1964, pp. 163-7.

ADAM, J. B. and SHAWCROSS, A. J. *The Language Laboratory*, viii, 72 pp. London: Pitman, 1963.

ADAMCZEWSKI, H. 'Un laboratoire de langues dans un lycée technique' *Lang. Mod.* no. 6, 1962, pp. 38-43.

ADAMS, J. 'Some thoughts on the use of the language laboratory and visual aids with advanced classes' *AVLJ* vol. 2, no. 4, Winter 1964/65, pp. 13-17.

AERTSENS, G. 'De bandopnemer in het moedertaalonderwijs' *Taalond.* vol. 7, no. 1, 1963.

AGER, D. E. 'Techniques in advanced language teaching' *AVLJ* vol. 5, no. 1, Summer 1967, pp. 5-10.

ALHINC, J. (and others) 'Laboratoire de langues et classes audio-visuelles'
Ét. Ling. App. (Besançon), no. 1, 1962, pp. 156-63. (See also *Lang. Mod.*
no. 5, 1962, pp. 55-62.)

ALHINC, J. 'Audio-visual methods in use at the Besançon Centre of Applied
Linguistics' *Research and Techniques for the Benefit of Modern Language Teach-
ing*, Strasbourg, Council for Cultural Co-operation of the Council of
Europe, 1964, pp. 119-32.

ALMAND, P. 'L'utilisation du magnétophone dans les classes de langues
vivantes' *Lang. Mod.* no. 2, 1964, pp. 63-4.

ANDERSON, E. W. 'Review and criticism' (Keating Report) *M.L.J.* vol. 48,
no. 4, April 1964, pp. 197-207.

ANTIER, M. 'Panorama de l'enseignement des langues vivantes en France'
Fr. Monde no. 35, Sept. 1965, pp. 15-21.

ANTROBUS, A. L. See MOORE, S. and ANTROBUS, A. L.

APELT, W. 'Situational Grammar—ein elementares Anliegen des modernen
Fremdsprachenunterrichts' *Fremdspr.* 9, no. 9, 1965.

APPLEGATE, J. R. 'Motion pictures in foreign language instruction' *Vis. Ed.*
April 1966, pp. 33-5.

BAGAGE, J. 'Emploi du magnétophone pour la classe d'anglais' *Lang. Mod.*
Sept. 1963, pp. 30-1.

BAUER, E. W. 'A study of the effectiveness of two language laboratory conditions in the teaching of second year German' *I.R.A.L.* vol. 2, no. 2, 1964,
pp. 99-112.

BEAL, M. *French Language Drills*, 288 pp. London: Macmillan, 1967.

BEAUMONT, A. J. 'A survey of language laboratory types' *Tech. Ed.* vol. 7, no. 8,
Aug. 1965, pp. 366-7.

BELILTY, S. See ENOCH, P. and BELILTY, S.

BELL, E. 'Radio and television in modern language teaching' *Vis. Ed.* Mar.
1962, pp. 8-11.

BENNETT, W. A. 'The integration of the language laboratory and classroom
teaching' *Vis. Ed.* Feb. 1964, pp. 7-9.

BENNETT, W. A. 'The role of the Language Centre' *Vis. Ed.* May 1964,
pp. 11-13.

BENNETT, W. A. 'The language laboratory' *Inc. Ling.* vol. 5, no. 2, Apr. 1966,
pp. 38-41.

BENNETT, W. A. *Language Laboratory List* (Occasional Papers 4) N.C.A.V.A.E.
May 1966.

BERLET, K. W. 'Audio-lingual method' *T.E.S.* 19 May 1967, p. 1712. (See
DAVIDSON, J.: 'Audio-visual method.')

BERTRAND, J. 'Apprentissage du langage, le lieu, la direction' *Fr. Monde.*
no. 7, Feb.-March 1962, pp. 32-4.

BIRNIE, J. R. and JOHNSON, I. R. 'Developments in language laboratory equipment and techniques. Part 1' *Vis. Ed.* June 1964, pp. 6-7.

BIRNIE, J. R. and JOHNSON, I. R. 'Developments in language laboratory equipment and techniques. Part 2—Material' *Vis. Ed.* April 1965, pp. 17-19.

BIRNIE, J. R. See JOHNSON, I. R. and BIRNIE, J. R.

BLEACKLEY, J. R. 'Audio-visual aids in primary schools: The Infants' Department' *Vis. Ed.* April 1966, pp. 7-8.

BOULOC, P. 'L'utilisation du film animé dans l'enseignement d'une langue vivante' *AVLJ*, vol. 4, no. 2, Winter 1966-7, pp. 75-82.

THE BRITISH COUNCIL—EDUCATIONAL AIDS DEPARTMENT. 'A Survey of language laboratory equipment' *British Council*, 1964, pp. 8. (Copies from State House, High Holborn, London, W.C.1.) Reprinted in *Ed. Teach.*, May 1964, pp. 51-9.

BROWN, J. J. and ROBINSON, G. A. 'Language laboratories—a new approach' *Tech. Ed.*, vol. 6, no. 6, June 1964, pp. 292-3.

BROWN, J. W. and THORNTON, J. W. Jr. *New Media in Higher Education.* Washington, D.C., Assoc. for Higher Educ. and Division of Audio-visual Instructional Service of the Nat. Educ. Assoc., 1964, pp. 182.

BROWN, T. H. 'Using visual cues as an aid for memorizing and dialogue' *M.L.J.* vol. 47, no. 8, Dec. 1963, pp. 363-6.

BUCKLE, P. 'Latin the easy way' *T.E.S.* 20 March, 1964, p. 728.

BUCKLEY, M. 'Contextualisation of language drills' *Mod. Lang.*, vol. 48, no. 4, Dec. 1967, pp. 165-70.

BUNG, K. A. 'Tape recorder in language classes' *AVLA News*, vol. 1, no. 3, Spring 1963. (Mimeographed.) (now *AVLJ*)

BUNG, K. A. 'Problems of "Learning" in the language laboratory' (1) *AVLJ*, vol. 2, no. 4, Winter 1964/65, pp. 3-7.
     Part (2) *AVLJ*, vol. 3, no. 1, Spring 1965, pp. 16-19.

BUNG, K. A. *Programmed Learning and the Language Laboratory—2* (collected papers). London: Longmac, 1967.

CABLE, R. *Audio-Visual Handbook.* London: U.L.P., 1965.

CARDWELL, R. A. 'The language laboratory as a teaching machine, equivocal response and psychological choice: an attempt at resolution' *AVLJ*, vol. 4, no. 2, Winter 1966-7, pp. 57-68.

CARTLEDGE, H. 'Film and tape' *E.L.T.*, vol. 17, no. 2, Jan. 1963, pp. 87-9.

CHAREST, G. J. 'The language laboratory and the human element in language teaching' *M.L.J.*, vol. 46, no. 6, Oct. 1962, p. 268.

CHATMAN, S. 'Report on possible applications of sound spectrography in the language laboratory' System Development Corporation Field Note FN-6817 Santa Monica, Aug. 20, 1962, 1-10.

CIOFFARI, D. C. 'The reasoning behind the pattern drill' *Can. M.L.R.*, vol. 19, no. 4, June 1963, pp. 8-13.

CIOFFARI, V. 'The influence of the Language Institute Program—past, present, and future' *M.L.J.*, vol. 46, Feb. 1962, pp. 62-8.

CLING, M. 'Le laboratoire de langues en Grande-Bretagne' *Lang. Mod.*, May-June 1963, pp. 48-52.

COLE, L. R. *Teaching French to Juniors*. London: U.L.P., 1964.

COLE, L. R. 'Some basic aspects of audio-visual and audio-lingual theory and technique' *AVLJ*, vol. 4, no. 1, Summer 1966, pp. 28-31.

COLE, L. R. 'Using a language laboratory course' *Mod. Lang.*, vol. 47, no. 4, Dec. 1966, pp. 151-6.

COLE, L. R. 'The visual element and the problem of meaning in language learning' *AVLJ*, vol. 4, no. 2, Winter 1966-7, pp. 84-7.

COLE, L. R. 'Applied Linguistics and the problem of meaning' *AVLJ*, vol. 4, no. 3, Spring 1967, pp. 107-10.

COMPANYS, E. 'Leçon de phonétique pour hispanophones' *Fr. Monde.*, no. 40, April-May 1966, pp. 28-30.

COPPEN, H. See LEE, W. R. and COPPEN, H.

CORDER, S. P. 'The language laboratory' *E.L.T.*, vol. 16, no. 4, July-Sept. 1962, pp. 184-8.

CORDER, S. P. 'A theory of visual aids in language teaching' *E.L.T.*, vol. 17, no. 2, Jan. 1963, pp. 82-7.

COTTAM, A. and GASKELL, J. M. 'Testing first-year Tavor' *Mod. Lang.*, vol. 47, no. 1, March 1966.

COUNCIL FOR CULTURAL CO-OPERATION OF THE COUNCIL OF EUROPE. *Recent Developments in Modern Language Teaching*. Education in Europe, Section 4, General. No. 1, Strasbourg, 1964.

New Trends in Linguistic Research. Education in Europe, Section 4, General. No. 2, Strasbourg, 1963.

New Research and Techniques for the Benefit of Modern Language Teaching. Education in Europe, Section 4, General. No. 3, Strasbourg, 1964.

Modern Language Teaching by Television. Education in Europe, Section 4. General. No. 4, Strasbourg, 1965.

Education and Cultural Films—Experiments in European Co-Production. Education in Europe, Section 4. General. No. 5, Strasbourg, 1965.

Fifth Conference of European Ministers of Education, Vienna. October 1965. (Report prepared by Secretariat.)

CROCKER, A. H. and DAVIDSON, J. M. C. Introduction to *Experiments with Modified Language Laboratories*, N.C.A.V.A.E., Occasional Papers, 10, 1965.

CROMPTON, J. S. 'Progress with the mobile language laboratory' *Mod. Lang.*, vol. 47, no. 2, June 1966, pp. 54-5.

CROSSMAN, D. M. 'Reports of the Keating Report' *Am. Sch. and Univ.*, vol. 36, no. 4, Dec. 1963, pp. 35-8.

DAMOISEAU, R. 'Comment transformer en dialogues des textes narratifs' *Fr. Monde*, no. 42, July-Aug. 1966, pp. 40-3.

DAPPER, G. See KAMENEW, V. V. and DAPPER, G.

DARLINGTON, J. 'French by audio-visual methods in a Secondary Modern School' *Mod. Lang.*, vol. 43, no. 4, Dec. 1962, pp. 151-5.

DAVIDSON, J. 'Audio-visual method' (Discussion) *T.E.S.*, 19 May, 1967, p. 1713. (See BERLET, K. W.: Audio-lingual method.)

DAVIDSON, J. M. C. See CROCKER, A. H. and DAVIDSON, J. M. C.

DAYAN, F. E. 'Structural drills for first-year university French students' *Babel*, vol. 2, no. 3, Oct. 1966, pp. 8-10.

DELATTRE, G. 'Les différents types d'exercices structuraux' *Fr. Monde*, no. 41, June 1966, pp. 12-21.

DELATTRE, P. 'Une technique "audio-linguale" d'initiation au français' *Fr. Monde*, no. 13, Dec. 1962, pp. 15-17.

DELATTRE, P. 'Quality in tape recording and voicing' *I.J.A.L.*, vol. 29, no. 2, April 1963, Pt. 3, pp. 55-9.

DELLACIO, C. 'The New Look in actual practice' *Hisp.*, vol. 46, no. 3, Sept. 1963, pp. 600-604.

DILLER, E. See NEWMARK, G. and DILLER, E.

DUBOIS, G. 'Les diapositives couleurs et l'enseignement de l'anglais' *Lang. Mod.*, May-June 1963, pp. 40-7.

DUCRETET, P. R. 'Language laboratory programming' *Can. M.L.R.*, vol. 28, Winter 1962, pp. 12-15.

DUTTON, B. 'Linguistic behaviour and language learning' *Vis. Ed.*, March 1964, pp. 11-13.

DUTTON, B. 'The modern approach to language teaching' *Vida Hisp.*, vol. 12, no. 2, Summer 1964, pp. 17-19.
   And vol. 12, no. 3, Winter 1964, pp. 15-17.

DUTTON, B. 'Linguistics and language teaching' (1) *AVLJ*, vol. 2, no. 3, Summer 1964, pp. 8-11.
   'Linguistics and language teaching' (2) *AVLJ*, vol. 2, no. 4, Winter 1964-5, pp. 9-11.
   'Linguistics and language teaching' (3) *AVLJ*, vol. 3, no. 1, Spring 1965, pp. 36-9.

DUTTON, B. (Ed.) *A Guide to Modern Language Teaching Methods.* London: Cassell, 1965.

DUTTON, B. 'The essential language laboratory' *Vis. Ed.*, March 1967, pp. 15-21. (First published in N.C.A.V.A.E., Occasional Papers, 10, 1965.)

DYKSTRA, G. See FORSDALE, L. and DYKSTRA, G.

EAMES, H. 'Speaking with many tongues—a Bangor experiment' *T.E.S.*, 26 June, 1964, p. 1763.

EDLING, J. V. and others. 'Reports on the Keating Report' *Am. Sch. & Univ.*, vol. 36, no. 4, Dec. 1963.

EDWARDS, P. M. 'Problems in typing foreign language material' *Inc. Ling.*, vol. 4, no. 4, Oct. 1965, pp. 104-06.

EDWARDS, S. 'The use of audio-visual aids in Colleges of Education' (Part 1). *Vis. Ed.*, Feb. 1966, pp. 9-12. Part 2 in *Vis. Ed.*, March 1966, pp. 4-6.

ENOCH, P. and BELILTY, S. 'Enseignement audio-visuel du Français au lycée' (Compte-rendu analytique d'une expérience pédagogique) *AVLJ*, vol. 4, no. 3, Spring 1967, pp. 120-5.

FFOULKES-EDWARDS, K. 'Algorithms and the teaching of grammar' *AVLJ*, vol. 5, no. 1, Summer 1967, pp. 27-9.

FILIPOVIĆ, R. 'Audio-visual languages at the University of Zagreb. Principles and methods' *I.R.A.L.*, vol. 2, no. 1, April 1964, pp. 53-62.

FLEMING, G. 'Attitudes to modern language teaching aids' ("Humour and language teaching") *AVLJ*, vol. 3, no. 3, Spring 1966, pp. 119-25. (Paper read in May 1965 at the Institute of Education, Cambridge.)

FLEMING, G., SPALENY, E. and PEPRNIK, J. 'The didactic organisation of pictorial reality in the new language teaching media.' *Praxis*, vol. 14, no. 2, April/June 1967, pp. 160-174.

FLETCHER, D. J. 'French politics: the audio-visual approach' *AVLJ*, vol. 4, no. 1, Summer 1966, pp. 17-19.

FORRESTER, D. L. 'A look at American labs.' *AVLJ*, vol. 3, no. 3, Spring 1966, pp. 147-8.

FORSDALE, L. and DYKSTRA, G. 'An experimental method of teaching foreign langs. by means of 8 mm. sound film in cartridge-loading projectors' *L.L.*, vol. 13, no. 1, 1963, pp. 5-10.

FOX, J. D. 'The "do-it-yourself" language laboratory' *Mod. Lang.*, vol. 44, no. 4, Dec. 1963, pp. 156-8.

FRASER, D. C. 'Psychological aspects of the learning process' *AVLJ*, vol. 3, no. 2, Autumn 1965, pp. 59-75. (Paper read at the June Meeting of the London Branch of the Association for Programmed Learning.)

FRIEDMANN, D. M. 'The language laboratory and the audio-visual student' *AVLJ*, vol. 3, no. 3, Spring 1966, pp. 143-6.

FRIEDMANN, H. 'The teaching of modern languages by the C.R.E.D.I.F. audio-visual method' *Inc. Ling.*, vol. 1, no. 3, July 1962, pp. 72-7.

FRIEDMANN, H. 'An individual language laboratory' *Vis. Ed.*, Dec. 1962, pp. 7-9.

FRIEDMANN, H. 'Language laboratories—some conceptions and misconceptions' *Tech. Ed.*, vol. 5, no. 1, Jan. 1963, pp. 20-1, reprinted in *Education Today*, March 1963, pp. 39-41. Also in *Babel*, 25 April 1964.

FRIEDMANN, H. 'The language laboratory—minimum requirements from the teacher's angle' *Tech. Ed.*, vol. 5, no. 12, Dec. 1963, pp. 575-7. vol. 6, no. 1, Jan. 1964, pp. 30-2. vol. 6, no. 2, Feb. 1964, pp. 84-7.

FRIEDMANN, H. 'The new language requirements and the teacher' *Tech. J.*, vol. 3, no. 2, March 1965, pp. 11-13, and p. 17. Also in *Sound and Image*, 7 Sept. 1965.

FRIEDMANN, H. 'Tongues a-talking' *T.E.S.*, 17 April, 1964, p. 965.

FRIEDMANN, H. 'Audio-visual aids and audio-visual method' *Language Laboratories*, published by East Anglian Regional Advisory Council for Further Education, 1964. (Address given at Jesus College, Cambridge, 24 March, 1963.)

FRIEDMANN, H. 'Audio-visual aids and methods' *The Audio-Visual Approach to Language Teaching* (symposium), N.C.A.V.A.E., Sept. 1965.

FRINK, O. 'A design for an audio-electronic repeater' *M.L.J.*, vol. 48, no. 2, Feb. 1964, pp. 78-82.

GAARDER, B. and HUTCHINSON, J. C. *Brief analysis of the Keating Report*, U.S. Office of Educ., Washington 25, D.C., Oct. 1963.

GAGE, N. L. (Ed.). *Handbook of Research on Teaching*, Chicago: Rand McNally, 1963.

GASKELL, J. M. See COTTAM, A. and GASKELL, J. M.

GAUDIN, L. S. 'Language laboratory and advanced work' *M.L.J.*, vol. 46, no. 2, Feb. 1962, pp. 79-81.

GAUTHIER, A. 'Quelques possibilités d'utilisation du magnétophone en classe' *Fr. Monde*, no. 19, Sept. 1963, pp. 15-17.

GEFEN, R. 'A plea for more linguistics in second-language teaching' *AVLJ*, vol. 5, no. 1, Summer 1967, pp. 12-16.

GERLACH, V. S. 'Self-instruction in the A-V laboratory' *Vis. Ed.*, Aug./Sept. 1966, pp. 36-7. (Reprinted from *A.V.I.*, Feb. 1966.)

GOMMES-JUDGE, A. 'Evaluating students' progress in language learning' *AVLJ*, vol. 5, no. 1, Summer 1967, pp. 21-5.

GÖRNER, S. and SCHUBERT, K. R. 'Arbeit mit Magnethafttafeln und Magnetapplikationen' *Pädagogik*, 21, 1.

GOULD, A. 'Visuals overlooked . . . ?' *AVLJ*, vol. 4, no. 3, Spring 1967, pp. 112-14.

GRADISNIK, A. J. *A trial program in Spanish for the fifth and sixth grades using instructional television*, pres. publ. by the author: Supervisor of Foreign Languages, The Milwaukee Public Schools, 5225 West Vliet Street, Milwaukee 8, Wis. 1962, pp. 44.

GRAVIT, F. W. and VALDMAN, A. (eds.). *Structural Drill and the Language Laboratory: Report of the Third Language Laboratory Conference held at Indiana University*, March 29-31, 1962. (Indiana Univ. Research Center in Anthropology, etc. no. 27), xi, 224 pp. The Hague: Mouton, 1963. Also *I.J.A.L.*, vol. 29, no. 2, Part 3, April 1963.

GREEN, N. 'Furniture for a language laboratory' *AVLJ*, vol. 3, no. 2, Autumn 1965, pp. 82-6. (Reproduced from *The Engineer*, vol. 218, October 9, 1964, pp. 584-6.)

GREIMAS, A. 'Méthodes audio-visuelles et enseignement des langues' *Ét. Ling. App.*, vol. 1, 1962, pp. 137-55.

GRITTNER, F. M. 'The language laboratory—gadget or godsend?' *Wis. J. Ed.*, vol. 95, no. 10, May 1963, pp. 15-16.

GRITTNER, F. 'Shortcomings of language laboratory. Findings in the IAR Research Bulletin' *M.L.J.*, vol. 48, no. 4, April 1964, pp. 207-10.

GUENOT, J. and others. 'La lisibilité des vues fixes' *Ét. Ling. App.*, vol. 1, 1962, pp. 104-35.

GUENOT, J. 'Audio-visual teaching of English to beginners: an educational experiment in the second year elementary class (age: 8 years)' *Research and Techniques for the Benefit of Modern Language Teaching*. Strasbourg. Council for Cultural Co-operation of the Council of Europe, 1964, pp. 109-17.

GUENOT, J. 'Language laboratories and still pictures in modern language teaching' *I.J. Ad. Yth. Ed.*, vol. 26, no. 1, 1964, pp. 40-6.

HANZELI, V. E. 'Programmed learning in French: work in progress' *Fr. Rev.*, vol. 35, no. 6, May 1962, pp. 587-9.

HARGREAVES, P. H. 'Language teaching in further education' *AVLJ*, vol. 3, no. 3, Spring 1966, pp. 130-1.

HARRIS, R. See MUELLER, T. and HARRIS, R.

HARRISON, K. 'The electronic ear' *A.P.L. Newsletter*, no. 2, May 1963, p. 11.

HARVARD, J. 'Still pictures' *Vis. Ed.*, May 1961, pp. 2-3, reprinted in N.C.A.V.A.E., *Audio-Visual Aids and Modern Language Teaching (a symposium)*, London, 1962, 46 pp.

HASAN, R. *The Language of the 8-year-old Child* (Transcript and Computer Analysis) Nuffield Foundation, Foreign Languages Teaching Materials Project, Occasional Papers no. 5, 1964.

HAYES, A. S. *Language Laboratory Facilities: Technical Guide for their Selection, Purchase, Use and Maintenance*, vii, 119 pp. U.S. Office of Educ., Washington, 1963. New edition with Bibliography. London: O.U.P., 1968.

HEALEY, F. G. *Foreign Language Teaching in the Universities*, ix, 271 pp. Manchester University Press, 1967.

HENNING, W. A. 'Discrimination training and self-evaluation in the teaching of pronunciation.' *I.R.A.L.*, vol. 4, no. 1, 1966, pp. 7-17.

HEPWORTH, J. B. *The Language Laboratory: A Bibliography*, Manchester Libraries Committee, 1966, Manchester Central Library.

HICKEL, R. *Modern Language Teaching by Television* (a survey based on the principal experiments carried out in Western Europe). Council for Cultural Co-operation of the Council of Europe, Education in Europe, Section 4, General. No. 4, Strasbourg, 1965.

HILL, D. 'The use of French records in the classroom' *Vis. Ed.*, Aug. 1962, pp. 17-19.

HILL, L. A. 'Some uses of the tape-recorder in and outside the English classroom' *E.L.T.*, vol. 15, no. 3, April-June 1961, pp. 116-19. Reprinted in *Selected Articles on the Teaching of English as a Foreign Language*. London: O.U.P., 1967.

HILTON, J. B. 'The language laboratory in the Grammar School' *Vis. Ed.*, Feb. 1963, pp. 3-4.

HILTON, J. B. *The Language Laboratory in School*, 150 pp. London: Methuen, 1964.

HILTON, M. 'Language laboratory exercises for post A-level students' *Mod. Lang.*, vol. 48, no. 4, Dec. 1967, pp. 151-5.

HITEN, E. and MIKUS-PERREAL, R. 'La bande sonore' *Fr. Rev.*, vol. 37, no. 6, May 1964, pp. 675-82.

HOBSON, P. T. *A Discussion on the Care and Maintenance of Tape Recorders for Language Laboratories.*

A Discussion on Magnetic Tapes for Language Teaching. Minnesota Mining and Manufacturing Co. Ltd.

HOCKING, C. S. W. 'Language lab., 2: the answer to industry's language problem?' *Inc. Ling*, vol. 3, no. 1, Jan. 1964, pp. 5-8.

HOCKING, E. 'Methods and techniques in transition' *Fr. Rev.*, vol. 35, no. 4, Feb. 1962, pp. 396-401.

HOCKING, E. *The Language Laboratory and Language Learning.* 212 pp. Dept. of A-V. Instruction, National Education Association, Washington, 1964 (DAVI Monographs, no. 2).

HOCKING, E. 'De l'audio-visuelle à l'enseignement de la civilisation' *Fr. Monde*, no. 44, Oct.-Nov. 1966, pp. 42-3.

HOCKING, E. 'Audio-lingual reading' *M.L.J.*, vol. 51, no. 5, May 1967, pp. 264-7.

HORWOOD, E. K. (compiler) 'Various types of language laboratory.' *AVLJ*, vol. 2, no. 3, Summer 1964, pp. 20-7. (The article is a summary of methods currently in use in language laboratories and is taken from MARTY, F. L. *Language Laboratory Learning.*)

HUEBENER, T. 'The new key is now off-key!' *M.L.J.*, vol. 47, no. 8, Dec. 1963, pp. 375-7.

HUMESKY, A. 'Structural drills as the basis of instruction in Russian.' *I.J.A.L.*, vol. 29, no. 2, Part 3, April 1963, pp. 113-17.

HUTCHINSON, J. C. See GAARDER, B. and HUTCHINSON, J. C.

INGRAM, S. 'Aural aids: gramophone and tape-recorder' *Vis. Ed.*, June 1961, pp. 5-8. Reprinted in N.C.A.V.A.E., *Audio-Visual Aids and Modern Language Teaching* (a symposium), London, 1962, 46 pp.

INGRAM, S. 'Audio-visual French: the Tavor System' *Vis. Ed.*, Sept., 1961, pp. 2-5. Reprinted in N.C.A.V.A.E., *Audio-Visual Aids and Modern Language Teaching* (a symposium), London, 1962, 46 pp.

INGRAM, S. and MACE, J. 'Audio-visual French, further experiments' *Mod. Lang.*, vol. 44, no. 1, March 1963, pp. 23-30.

INGRAM, S. R. 'The modern language scene' *Vis. Ed.*, Jan. 1967, pp. 9-12.

INTERNATIONAL AUDIO-VISUAL TECHNICAL CENTRE. *Audio-Visual Aids and Teaching of Languages: Bibliographical References.* I.A.V.T.C., Bell Foundation, Antwerp, Belgium, April 1963.

IVES, D. G. 'A modified language laboratory' *Vis. Ed.*, Dec. 1966, pp. 7-10. (Reprinted in N.C.A.V.A.E., Occasional Papers 10, 1965.)

JAESCHKE, G. 'Zur methodischen Aufbereitung von Tonbändern für den Russischunterricht in einem Sprachkabinett' *Fremdspr.*, No. 4, 1966.

JAMESON, A. See KAY, J. B. and JAMESON, A.

JOHNSON, I. R. and BIRNIE J. R. 'Language laboratory system without booths.' *E.L.T.*, vol. 18, no. 4, July 1964, pp. 181-3.

JOHNSON, I. R. See BIRNIE, J. R. and JOHNSON, I. R.

JONES, J. G. *Teaching with Tape*, Focal Press, 1962, 160 pp.

JUST, F. P. See SCOTT, S. J. and JUST, F. P.

KAMENEW, V. V. and DAPPER, G. 'The price of sight and sound' *AVLJ*, vol. 4, no. 3, Spring 1967, pp. 116-18.

KAY, J. B. and JAMESON, A. 'A classification and retrieval system for recorded foreign language tapes.' *I.R.A.L.*, vol. 5, no. 4, 1967, pp. 195-200.

KEATING, R. F. *A Study of the Effectiveness of Language Laboratories: a Preliminary Evaluation of Twenty-one School Systems of the Metropolitan School Study Council.* Institute of Administrative Research, Teachers College, Columbia University, New York, 1963, x, 61 pp.

KELLERMANN, M. *Two Experiments on Language Teaching in Primary Schools in Leeds.* Nuffield Foundation, 1964, 77 pp.

KENRICK, D. S. 'Transformational grammar and the language teacher' *AVLJ*, vol. 5, no. 1, Summer 1967, pp. 18-19.

KHARKOVSKIL, Z. 'Tipovoe oborudovanie shkolnogo kabineta inostrannykh yazykov' *Inostran. Yazyki*, no. 2, 1963, pp. 77-83.

KIRCH, M. S. 'Visual or graphic?' *M.L.J.*, vol. 46, no. 1, Jan. 1962, p. 37.

KIRCH, M. S. 'The role of the language laboratory' *M.L.J.*, vol. 47, no. 6, Oct. 1963, pp. 256-60.

KIST, J. C., RENARD, C., & LAUER, H. *Teaching with Voix et Images de France, Premier Degré* (Preliminary Edition). Issued by: Center for Curriculum Development in A-V Language Teaching. Published by: Chilton Books, Philadelphia and New York, 1963, Third Printing March 1965, 180 pp., indexes.

KREUSLER, A. 'How Soviet schools use A-V tools in language study' *A.V.I.*, vol. 7, no. 5, May 1962, p. 292.

LADO, R. *Language Teaching: a Scientific Approach.* New York: McGraw Hill, 1964, 239 pp.

LADO, R. See ORNSTEIN, J. and LADO, R.

LAMERAND, R. 'The language laboratory and the study of literature' *Babel*, vol. 2, no. 1, Apr. 1966.

LANE, H. L. 'Specification for auditory discrimination learning' *I.J.A.L.*, vol. 29, no. 2, Part 3, April 1963, pp. 60-69.

'LANGUAGE LABORATORIES. A guide to design and equipment' *Arch. J.*, vol. 140, no. 25, Dec. 16, 1964, Information Sheet 1307, p. 4.

LAUER, H. See KIST, J. C., RENARD, C., and LAUER, H.

LEE, W. R. and COPPEN, H. *Simple Audio-Visual Aids to Foreign Language Teaching*, 122 pp. London: O.U.P., 1964.

LEESON, R. 'Oral composition with advanced students: an integrated technique' *AVLJ*, vol. 4, no. 2, Winter 1966-7, pp. 69-73.

LEIDY, T. R. *Achievement in Modern Languages as a Function of Variations in Language Laboratory Facilities: a Thesis Submitted to the Faculty of Purdue University*. Ann Arbor, Univ. Microfilms Inc., 1963, 134 pp.

LEON, P. *Laboratoire de langues et Correction phonétique*, Didier, Rand, 1962, 275 pp. (incl. 23 pp. Bibliog.). (Publications du Centre de Linguistique Appliquée de Besançon.)

LEPENDIN, V. 'Kabinet inostrannogo yazyka' *Inostran. Yazyki* no. 4, 1963, pp. 95-104.

LEVY, H. 'Teaching French in the Secondary Modern School' *Mod. Lang.*, vol. 43, no. 4, Dec. 1962, pp. 148-50.

LIBBISH, B. (ed). *Advances in the Teaching of Modern Languages*, vol. 1, 175 pp. London: Pergamon, 1964.

LIVINGSTONE, L. 'Organic versus functional grammar in the audio-lingual approach' *M.L.J.*, vol. 46, no. 7, Nov. 1962, pp. 304-07.

LOCKE, P. J. 'Language laboratories' *Vida Hisp.*, vol. 11, no. 1, Spring 1963, pp. 23-6.

LOVEDAY, L. C. 'Choosing a language laboratory' *Mod. Lang.*, vol. 45, no. 4, Dec. 1964, pp. 158-60.

LUBBOCK, D. C. 'Language laboratory at Southend College of Technology' *Off. Arch.*, vol. 27, Sept. 1964, pp. 1057-61.

MACE, J. See INGRAM, S. and MACE, J.

MACKEY, W. F. *Language Teaching Analysis*, xi, 554 pp. (inc. bibliography and index). London: Longmans, 1965.

MACNEILL, G. H. 'The language laboratory: its method and practice' *Can. M.L.R.*, vol. 8, no. 3, Spring 1962, pp. 54-6.

MALANDRIN, S. See MIALARET, G. and MALANDRIN, C.

MARTY, F. *Linguistics—Applied to the Beginning French Course*, Roanoke, Virginia: A-V Publications, 1963.

MARTY, F. 'A-V for self-instructional language courses' *Ed. Screen*, May 1963, pp. 266-7.

MARTY, F. *Language Laboratory Learning*. Roanoke, Virginia: A-V Publications, 1965.

MATHIEU, G. 'Language laboratories' *Rev. Ed. Res.*, vol. 32, no. 2, April 1962, pp. 168-78.

MATHIEU, G. 'The pause lever: key to self-pacing' *Gmn. Qtly.*, vol. 35, no. 3, May 1962, pp. 318-21.

MATHIEU, G. 'Pitfalls of pattern practice: an exegesis' *M.L.J.*, vol. 48, no. 1 Jan, 1964, pp. 20-4.

MATHIEU, G. 'Pause control: a device for self-pacing in the language lab.' *A.V.I.*, vol. 9, no. 6, June 1964, p. 352.

MATHIEU, G. 'Techniques de laboratoire de langues pour les exercices structuraux' *Fr. Monde*, no. 43, Sept. 1966, pp. 25-8.

MATLUCK, J. 'Notes on the "modified" Lab. Library system' *M.L.J.*, vol. 47, no. 1, Jan. 1963, pp. 20-2.

MAYNES, J. O., Jr. 'An experiment to gauge the effectiveness of the audio-lingual method and the language lab.' *Hisp.*, vol. 45, no. 2, May 1962, pp. 377-82.

MAYO, H. 'Class, laboratory, and credit hours in beginning modern languages' *M.L.J.*, vol. 47, no. 1, Jan. 1963, pp. 23-5.

MEALOR, V. 'An antennae [*sic*] on the roof' *New Ed.*, vol. 1, no. 6, April 1965, pp. 29-32.

MEIER, A. 'Modell des Unterrichts mit hochschulähnlichen Lehr—und Lernformen in den oberen Klassen' *Pädagogik*, 20/12.

MENDELOFF, H. 'Aural placement by television' *M.L.J.*, vol. 47, no. 3, March 1963, pp. 110-13.

MERAS, E. A. *A Language Teacher's Guide.* New York: Harper Row, 1962.

METSON, G. 'Illustration or visual aid—finding the questions' *AVLJ*, vol. 4, no. 1, Summer 1966, pp. 13-15.

MIALARET, G. and MALANDRIN, C. 'La perception du film fixe chez l'enfant' *Ét. Ling. App.*, vol. 1, 1962, pp. 95-103.

MIALARET, G. *The Psychology of the Use of Audio-Visual Aids in Primary Education*, Harrap/Unesco, 1966.

MICHALSKI, A. 'Language laboratory and language learning' *Hisp.*, vol. 45, no. 1, March 1962, pp. 175-7.

MIKESELL, N. L. 'Developing the recorded materials library' *I.J.A.L.*, vol. 29, no. 2, Part 3, April 1963, pp. 195-204.

MIKUS-PERREAL, R. See HITEN, E. and MIKUS-PERREAL, R.

MILDENBERGER, K. W. 'Problems, perspectives and projections: materials and techniques for the language laboratory' *I.J.A.L.*, vol. 28, no. 1, Jan. 1962.

MILLS, W. 'The teaching machine in the language class' *Vis. Ed.*, May 1962.

MOORE, J. M. 'Break-through in foreign languages: the audio-lingual approach' *J. Sec. Ed.* (Amer.), vol. 38, no. 6, Oct. 1963, pp. 8-12.

MOORE, P. 'A language laboratory experiment in the junior high-school' *M.L.J.*, vol. 46, no. 6, Oct. 1962, pp. 269-71.

MOORE, S. and ANTROBUS, A. L. *An Introduction to the Language Laboratory*, Nuffield Foundation, Foreign Language Teaching Materials Project, Reports and Occasional Papers, no. 2, 1964.

MOULTON, W. G. 'What is structural drill?' *I.J.A.L.*, vol. 29, no. 2, Part 3, April 1963, pp. 3-15.

MUELLER, K. A. and WIERSMA, W. 'The effects of language laboratory type upon cultural orientation scores of foreign language students' *M.L.J.*, vol. 51, no. 5, May 1967, pp. 258-63.

MUELLER, K. A. and WIERSMA, W. 'The effects of language laboratory type upon foreign language achievement scores' *M.L.J.*, vol. 51, no. 6, Oct. 1967, pp. 349-51.

MUELLER, T. 'Correlating the lang. lab. with textbook: some basic considerations' *I.J.A.L.*, vol. 29, no. 2, Part 3, April 1963, pp. 83-9.

MUELLER, T. and HARRIS, R. 'First year College French through an audio-lingual program' *I.R.A.L.*, vol. 4, no. 1, 1966, pp. 19-38.

MUIR, B. W. 'An ideal language laboratory' *Babel*, vol. 3, no. 2, July 1967, p. 31 and p. 33.

MÜLLER, M. *Report of International Conference on Modern Foreign Language Teaching*, Aug. 31st-Sept. 5th 1964, Berlin. (Pädagogisches Zentrum, Berlin), Cornelsen.

MYRON, H. B. 'Languages, cultures and better lectures' *Fr. Rev.*, Dec. 1963, pp. 176-81.

NAJAM, E. (ed.). *Materials and Techniques for the Language Laboratory*, Publications of the research centre in Anthropology, etc. no. 18 (1962), also *I.J.A.L.*, vol. 28, no. 1, Part 2, Jan. 1962. Report of the second Language Laboratory Conference held at Purdue University, March 23-25, 1961, Indiana Univ. Bloomington 1961, x, 218 pp., Mouton, 1962.

N.C.A.V.A.E. *Audio-Visual Aids and Modern Language Teaching* (a symposium), London, 1962, 46 pp. (Articles first published in *Vis. Ed.*, June 1961-March 1962.)

N.C.A.V.A.E. *Experiments with Modified Language Laboratories*, Occasional Papers 10, 1965.

NEWMARK, G. and DILLER, E. 'Emphasizing the audio in the audio-lingual approach' *M.L.J.*, vol. 48, no. 1, Jan. 1964, pp. 18-20.

NEWMARK, P. 'Conflict in teaching methods' *Ad. Ed.*, vol. 34, no. 5, Jan. 1962, pp. 238-48.

NEWMARK, P. 'Some thoughts on machines and language teachers' *Ad. Ed.*, vol. 36, no. 6, March 1964, pp. 311-19.

NEWMARK, P. P. 'What language laboratories can do' *Inc. Ling.*, vol. 5, no. 2, April 1966, pp. 42-8.

ODENTHAL, C. 'Teachers of German in Evening Institutes still reluctant to adopt the audio-visual method?' *AVLJ*, vol. 4, no. 1, Summer 1966, pp. 36-7. (Report of a short introductory course at Holborn College of Law, Languages and Commerce to introduce Evening Institute Instructors of German to A-V Methods, etc. April-May 1966).

O'NEAL, R. 'For a new look at laboratory planning' *Fr. Rev.*, no. 37, Feb. 1964, pp. 453-5.

ORNA, B. 'Prague—"Teaching Aids" Centre' *Vis. Ed.*, Feb. 1965, pp. 4-5.

ORNSTEIN, J. and LADO, R. 'Research in foreign language teaching methodology' *I.R.A.L.*, vol. 5, no. 1, 1967, pp. 11-25.

ORR, J. 'Language teaching and audio-visual aids. A selective bibliography' *A.V.I.*, vol. 7, no. 9, Nov. 1962.

ORWEN, G. P. 'Aid for the language laboratory' *M.L.J.*, vol. 46, no. 1, Jan. 1962, pp. 39-40.

OSMAN, N. 'Objective tests of an aural-oral command of French' *Babel*, vol. 1, no. 2, July 1965, pp. 2-8.

OSMAN, N. 'Objective tests of a reading-writing command of French' *Babel*, vol. 1, no. 3, Oct. 1965, pp. 3-10.

PANETH, E. 'The teacher's apprentice' *Mod. Lang.*, vol. 45, no. 2, June 1964, pp. 68-73.

PANETH, E. 'Tapes on tap' *AVLJ*, vol. 3, no. 3, Spring 1966, pp. 127-9.

PARKER, A. 'Fluency through film' *Vis. Ed.*, Oct. 1961, pp. 8-9. Reprinted in N.C.A.V.A.E. *Audio-visual aids and modern language teaching* (a symposium). London, 1962, 46 pp.

PEPRNIK, J. See FLEMING, G., SPALENY, E. and PEPRNIK, J.

PIRTLE, W. G. 'A multiple response device in foreign language learning' *M.L.J.*, vol. 48, no. 1, Jan. 1964, pp. 39-40.

PLASTRE, G. 'Réflexions sur la méthodologie audio-visuelle structuro-globale en regard des principes généraux de la didactique des langues secondes' *Rev. Phon. App.*, no. 3, 1966.

POLITZER, R. L. 'Some reflections on pattern practice' *M.L.J.*, vol. 48, no. 1, Jan. 1964, pp. 24-8.

POMERANZ, F. 'The language laboratory' *Progress*, no. 1, 1965.

POMERANZ, F. 'Training future export executives' *Manager*, March 1965.

POMERANZ, F. 'An audio-visual audio-lingual series of courses for businessmen' *AVLJ*, vol. 3, no. 3, Spring 1966, pp. 134-6.

POMERANZ, F. 'Languages for industry' *AVLJ*, vol. 4, no. 3, Spring 1967, pp. 130-5. (Reprinted from *Unilever Quarterly*.)

POND, K. S. 'A language teaching tool: the overhead projector' *M.L.J.*, vol. 47, no. 1, Jan. 1963, pp. 30-3.

PROBYN, H. E. 'Audio-visual language teaching and equipment: some new suggestions' *AVLJ*, vol. 3, no. 1, Spring 1965, pp. 25-6.

PROBYN, H. E. 'The direct visual approach in modern language teaching' *Vis. Ed.*, June 1965, pp. 11-12.

PROBYN, H. E. 'The role of the monitor in the language laboratory' *AVLJ*, vol. 3, no. 3, Spring 1966, pp. 137-41.

PROCTOR, L. 'Self-instruction in the language laboratory' *AVLJ*, vol. 4, no. 1, Summer 1966, pp. 5-12.

PURVES, F. *The Philips Tape Recording Book*, London: Focal Press, 1962.

QUINN, T. J. 'Language laboratories—some comments' *Babel*, no. 23, July 1963, pp. 15-18.

RAPOPORT, A. 'Foreign languages on tape' *Inc. Ling.*, vol. 1, no. 1, Jan. 1962, p. 26.

RAWSON-JONES, K. 'A non-integrated language laboratory programme' *Vis. Ed.*, Jan. 1967, pp. 29-31.

REGENSTREIF, H. 'Why stop at language laboratories?' *A.V.I.*, vol. 7, no. 5, May 1962, p. 282.

REINDORP, R. C. 'Role of the laboratory in the foreign language program' *Hisp.*, vol. 45, no. 4, Dec. 1962, pp. 829-36.

RENARD, C. See KIST, J. C., RENARD, C. and LAUER, H.

RENARD, R. *La méthode audio-visuelle et structuro-globale de St. Cloud-Zagreb*, 127 pp. Paris: Didier, 1964.

RICHARDSON, G. 'The visual element in audio-visual aids' *Mod. Lang.*, vol. 47, no. 2, June 1966, pp. 76-9.

RIDDER, L. DE. 'Emploi du magnétophone pour le travail par demigroupes en classe de 6e' *Lang. Mod.*, vol. 1, 1964, pp. 38-9.

RIVENC, P. 'Two audio-visual methods of teaching French as a foreign language' *Research and Techniques for the Benefit of Modern Language Teaching.* Strasbourg, Council for Cultural Co-operation of the Council of Europe, 1964, pp. 93-108.

RIVENC, P. 'Formation des enseignants et techniques audio-visuelles' *Fr. Monde*, no. 25, June 1964, pp. 10-13.

RIVERS, W. M. *The Psychologist and the Foreign Language Teacher*, vii, 212 pp. University of Chicago Press, 1964.

RIVERS, W. M. 'Tape recorders and language laboratories' *Sec. Teach.*, 103, 1965.

ROBINSON, D. 'Eight-year olds in the language laboratory' *Vis. Ed.*, Oct. 1962, pp. 10-11.

ROBINSON, G. A., See BROWN, J. J. and ROBINSON, G. A.

ROCHE, N. 'Préparation à l'expression écrite' *Fr. Monde*, no. 39, March 1966, pp. 24-26.

ROEMMELE, J. A. 'The language laboratory—a practical experiment' *E.L.T.*, vol. 18, no. 3, April 1964, pp. 122-5.

ROWE, H. M. 'The well qualified foreign language teacher' *Babel*, vol. 1, no. 1, Apr. 1965, pp. 13-15.

ROWNTREE, J. 'Language by radio' *Ad. Ed.*, vol. 34, no. 5, Jan. 1962, pp. 264-6 (also p. 349).

SACKS, N. P. 'Structural drill, current Spanish textbooks, and the language laboratory' *I.J.A.L.*, April 1963, vol. 29, no. 2, Part 3, pp. 103-12.

SAGER, J. C. 'Material for the language laboratory' *AVLJ*, vol. 3, no. 1, Spring 1965, pp. 5-8.

SAGER, J. C. 'Pattern drills in the language laboratory' *Inc. Ling.*, vol. 4, no. 3, July 1965, pp. 70-2.

SAGER, J. C. 'Cataloguing and administering a tape collection for the language laboratory' *AVLJ*, vol. 4, no. 1, Summer 1966, pp. 20-23.

SAGER, J. C. *German Structure Drills*, x, 228 pp. London; Pitman, 1967.

SANCHEZ, J. 'Twenty years of modern language laboratory: an annotated bibliography' *M.L.J.*, vol. 43, no. 5, May 1959, pp. 228-32.

SANCHEZ, J. (compiler). 'Audio-visual aids' *M.L.J.*, vols. 40 (1956)–49 (1965).

SCHANK, L. H. 'Self-contained 8 mm. sound language teaching machine' *J.S.M.P.T.E.*, Sept. 1963, pp. 682-4.

SCHERER, G. A. C. and WERTHEIMER, M. *A Psycho-linguistic Experiment in Foreign Language Teaching*, New York: McGraw Hill, 1964.

SCHERTZ, P. 'Techniques audio-visuelles et classe de conversation' *Fr. Monde*, no. 13, Dec. 1962.

SCHUBERT, K. R. See GÖRNER, S. and SCHUBERT, K. R.

SCOTT, S. J. and JUST, F. P. 'An open letter to modern language methodists' *Babel*, no. 24, Oct. 1963, p. 34.

SCULTHORPE, M. A. L. 'The language laboratory' *Ad. Ed.*, vol. 34, no. 5, Jan. 1962, pp. 249-53. (Reprinted from *Vis. Ed.*, Nov. 1961.)

SCULTHORPE, M. A. L. 'Language laboratory progress' *Vis. Ed.*, March 1963, pp. 6-9.

SCULTHORPE, M. A. L. 'The language laboratory: 1. its role in adult language courses' *Inc. Ling.*, vol. 3, no. 1, Jan. 1964, pp. 2-3.

SEGUIN, E. See SPENCER, R. E. and SEGUIN, E.

SHAWCROSS, A. J. See ADAM, J. B. and SHAWCROSS, A. J.

SILIAKUS, H. J. 'A note on the effective use of the language laboratory' *Babel*, vol. 1, no. 3, Oct. 1965, p. 33.

SILVA, J. 'Language laboratory performance. A quick glance' *Ed. Screen*, vol. 41, no. 10. Oct. 1962. p. 600.
Also in *Ed. D.*, vol. 28, Dec. 1962, pp. 42-3.

SMITH, E. T. 'The language laboratory in the United States' *Ad. Ed.*, vol. 34, no. 5, Jan. 1962, pp. 284-5.

SMITH, M. 'Taping oral exams' *T.E.S.*, 12 March 1965, p. 737.

SPALENY, E. See FLEMING, G., SPALENY, E. and PEPRNIK, J.

SPENCER, R. E. and SEGUIN, E. L. 'The relative effectiveness of earphones and loudspeakers as a means of presenting a listening test in a foreign language' *M.L.J.*, vol. 48, Oct. 1964, pp. 346-9.

SPICER, A. and others. *Audio-visual French courses for primary schools: an annotated bibliography*, 70 pp. Nuffield Foundation, Foreign Languages Teaching Materials Project, Reports and Occasional Papers, no. 3, 1965.

STACK, E. M. (ed.). 'Visual aids for the laboratory' *E.T.L. Newsletter*, vol. 4, no. 3, March 1963, pp. 1-3.

STACK, E. M. *The Language Laboratory and Modern Language Teaching*, viii, 149 pp. New York: O.U.P., 1960. Revised edn. 1966.

STACK, E. M. 'Laboratories—the effectiveness controversy' *M.L.J.*, vol. 48, no. 4, April 1964, pp. 189-94.

STEVICK, E. W. *A Workbook in Language Teaching*. New York: Abingdon Press, 1962.

STEVICK, E. W. 'Structural drills in the laboratory' *I.J.A.L.*, vol. 29, no. 2, Part 3, April 1963, pp. 37-44.

STOCK, H. 'Students' opinions of the language laboratory' *Babel*, vol. 2, no. 3, Oct. 1966, pp. 24-7.

STORK, F. C. 'Linguistics and the teaching of modern languages' *Mod. Lang.*, vol. 46, no. 4, Dec. 1965, pp. 151-4.

STORK, F. C. 'The language laboratory—what it can and cannot do' *AVLJ*, vol. 4, no. 1, Summer 1966, pp. 33-5.

STREVENS, P. D. 'Recent British developments in language teaching' *Babel*, vol. 2, no. 2, July 1966, pp. 5-9.

STREVENS, P. D. 'Some observations on language laboratories' *Rev. Phon. App.* no. 5, 1967, pp. 75-81.

STUDHOLME, R. 'Das fliegende Sprachlabor' (in English) *Mod. Lang.*, vol. 44, no. 2, June 1963, pp. 72-4.

TENNANT, P. F. D. 'Language communication and misunderstanding' (Text of 6th Threlford Memorial Lecture) *Inc. Ling.*, vol. 5, no. 1, Jan. 1966, pp. 1-8.

THOMSON, F. P. 'The first language laboratory' *AVLA News* (now *AVLJ*), vol. 1, no. 3, Spring 1963 (mimeographed).

Thomson, F. P. 'Language laboratories' *Listener*, Nov. 14 1963, p. 794.

THOMSON, F. P. 'Teaching in a technological age' *Design*, 203/1965, pp. 36-47.

THOMSON, F. P. 'Teaching machines, language laboratories and programmed instruction techniques' *El. Sup.*, vol. 45, no. 12, Dec. 1965.

THORNTON, J. W., Jr. See BROWN, J. W. and THORNTON, J. W. Jr.

TOMATIS, A. *L'oreille et le langage*, 192 pp. Paris: Collections Microcosme, Éditions du Seuil, 1963.

TRIBNER, G. 'Zur Problematik des modernen Fremdsprachenunterrichts' *Fremdspr.*, no. 1, 1965.

TRUMP, J. 'Tomorrow's schools' *Vis. Ed.*, April 1962, pp. 2-5.

TURNER, D. 'Occupation: language laboratory director' *M.L.J.*, vol. 48, no. 3, March 1964, pp. 151-4.

TURNER, J. D. *Introduction to the Language Laboratory*, 110 pp. London: U.L.P., 1965.

TURNER, J. D. *Language Laboratories in Great Britain* 1965, Third edition, 93 pp. London: U.L.P., 1965.

TYSON, D. A. 'Pastures new for the "Milking Machine"' *Vis. Ed.*, June 1966, pp. 26-7 (Reprinted in N.C.A.V.A.E. Occasional Papers 10, 1965).

UMBACH, W. R. 'A funnel for the foolish' *N.D.E.A. F.L.News*, vol. 3, no. 4, May 1964, pp. 1-4.

University Grants Committee and others. *Audio-Visual Aids in Higher Scientific Education: Report of the Committee Appointed in February 1963;* by the University Grants Committee, Dept. of Ed. and Science, Scottish Ed. Dept., 153 pp. H.M.S.O., 1965.

Uthess, H. 'Vorüberlegungen zur Erarbeitung von Unterrichtsmaterialen für die Arbeit in audiovisuellen Fremdsprachenkabinetten' *Fremdspr.*, no. 1-2, 1967.

Valdman, A. 'How do we break the lockstep?' *A.V.I.*, vol. 7, no. 9, Nov. 1962, pp. 630-4.

Valdman, A. 'Toward self-instruction in foreign language learning' *I.R.A.L.*, vol. 2, no. 1, April 1964, pp. 1-36.

Valdman, A. 'Toward a redefinition of teacher role and teaching content in foreign language instruction' *M.L.J.*, vol. 48, no. 5, May 1964, pp. 275-84.

Valdman, A. See Gravit, F. W. and Valdman, A.

Van Abbé, D. 'Languages in a hurry' *Tech. J.*, vol. 2, no. 5 (new series), June 1964, pp. 13-15.

Van Abbé, D. 'Overcoming initial difficulties' *Inc. Ling.*, vol. 4, no. 2, April 1965, pp. 46-8.

Van Der Will, W. 'The language laboratory in advanced language teaching' *Mod. Lang.*, vol. 47, no. 2, June 1966, pp. 56-8.

Varley, J. 'Selective and annotated report on films in the fields of linguistics, language teaching and related subjects' *Ling. Rep.*, vol. 6, no. 3 (Supp. No. 12), June 1964.

Vernon, P. (ed.). *The audio-visual approach to modern language teaching*, 72 pp. N.C.A.V.A.E. (Revised Edition), Sept. 1965.

Vernon, P. J. 'The use of language laboratories in Great Britain' (N.C.A.V.A.E., Occasional Papers 1, 1965). *Vis. Ed. Yearbook*, 1965, pp. 4-15.

Waddington, M. 'Foreign languages in the primary school' *Education Libraries Bulletin*, University of London, Institute of Education, Spring 1963.

Wagner, R. L. 'À propos de grammaires' *Fr. Monde*, no. 40, April-May 1966, pp. 14-22.

Wakeman, A. 'The language laboratory as an integrated part of a teaching programme' *Vis. Ed.*, May 1966. pp. 36-7.

Walker, R. M. 'The learning of related languages' *AVLJ*, vol. 3, no. 3, Spring 1966, pp. 113-17.

Warburton, J. 'Some uses of the language laboratory in post O-level modern language studies' *AVLJ*, vol. 4, no. 2, Winter 1966-7, pp. 89-92.

Warden, J. G. 'Suggestions for a course in oral translation' *Inc. Ling.*, vol. 5, no. 3, July 1966, pp. 70-6.

Wertheimer, M. See Scherer, G. A. C. and Wertheimer, M.

Wharram, D. 'Tapes and tape recorders' *AVLJ*, vol. 2, no. 1, Winter 1963, p. 22; vol. 2, no. 3, Summer 1964, pp. 16-17.

WHITEHOUSE, J. C. 'First encounter: introducing groups to a language laboratory' *Inc. Ling.*, vol. 3, no. 2, April 1964, pp. 43-4.

WIERSMA, W. See MUELLER, K. A. and WIERSMA, W.

WILLEKE, O. 'Ein Sprachlabor im Dienste des Klassenunterrichts' *I.R.A.L.*, vol. 2, no. 4, 1964, pp. 303-11.

WILLIAMS, I. C. 'The language laboratory' *Tech. Ed.*, vol. 4, no. 9, Sept. 1962, pp. 12-14.

WILLS, F. M. 'New developments in modern languages in the technological universities' *Mod. Lang.*, vol. 47, no. 1, March 1966, pp. 13-15, and Part 2, vol. 47, no. 2, June 1966, pp. 50-4.

WRIGHT, N. P. 'Audio-visual work with a language laboratory' *Mod. Lang.*, vol. 45, no. 3, Sept. 1964, pp. 104-11.

WRIGHT, N. P. 'The sixth form in the language laboratory' *Mod. Lang.*, vol. 48, no. 2, June 1967, pp. 77-80.

ZELDNER, M. 'The bewildered modern language teacher' *M.L.J.*, vol. 47, no. 6, Oct. 1963, pp. 245-53.

ZWEIBACK, E. 'The engrained patterns of the mother tongue relative to language learning and with reference to audio-visual aids' *AVLA News* (now *AVLJ*), vol. 1, no. 2, October 1962 (mimeographed).

ZWEIBACK, E. A. 'Two aspects of audio-visual language teaching' *AVLJ*, vol. 2, no. 3, Summer 1964, pp. 3-8.

J. B. KAY